## She felt trapped in a hideous nightmare

Dove had assured herself philosophically that the betrothal ceremony meant nothing, merely a charade that had to be played out.

But Marc's serious expression as a tall Arab stepped forward to throw a handkerchief over Marc's and Sheik Rahma's joined hands didn't lighten her fears. She began to shake as Rahma solemnly intoned: "I betroth thee my daughter Dove, the virgin, for a dowry of one thousand pounds."

She felt that she had wandered into a world of unreality, the dim faceless crowd a mirage, the deeply religious ceremony a hallucination. Her senses reeled and through the pounding in her ears she heard Marc's crisp, decisive reply: "I accept her betrothal from thee...."

OTHER
*Harlequin Romances*
by MARGARET ROME

Many of these titles are available at your local bookseller
or through the Harlequin Reader Service.

For a free catalogue listing all available Harlequin Romances,
send your name and address to:

HARLEQUIN READER SERVICE,
M.P.O. Box 707, Niagara Falls, N.Y. 14302
Canadian address: Stratford, Ontario, Canada N5A 6W2

or use coupon at back of book.

# Son of Adam

by

## MARGARET ROME

**Harlequin Books**

TORONTO • LONDON • NEW YORK • AMSTERDAM
SYDNEY • HAMBURG • PARIS

Original hardcover edition published in 1978
by Mills & Boon Limited

ISBN 0-373-02235-2

Harlequin edition published February 1979

Printed in U.S.A.

# CHAPTER ONE

Dove manoeuvred her white Mini into a parking space outside her parents' shop and before alighting sat for a moment contemplating the plate-glass window behind which was displayed an assortment of magazines, paperbacks, dummy packs of various brands of cigarettes and tobacco, and the usual array of wide-necked glass jars filled with sweets, chewing gum and other novelties guaranteed to tempt children to part with their pocket money.

She frowned. Things looked the same yet were in some way different. She tried to pinpoint the indefinable change and discovered a clue in a bedraggled bow of scarlet ribbon lying limp against the lid of a chocolate box, and a second in the curled-up yellowed pages of magazines left too long exposed to the sun. As she stepped out of the car to peer closely through the window her misgivings grew. A grimy veil of dust had settled upon the window display, unwrapped sweets had been allowed to melt inside of jars and then solidify into a hard, permanent mass; magazines and books were the ones she herself had set out when helping to change the window last time she was home, four months ago, and stuck in one corner was a dusty cardboard box, its contents shimmering in the sun. Christmas tree baubles on display in the middle of April! Undoubtedly some misfortune had befallen her meticulous father and her fanatically tidy mother.

Hurriedly she swung on her heel and almost ran around the corner of the building towards a side door that gave access to the flat above the shop, feeling a mixture of exasperation and worry, prepared to reprimand her father for omitting any reference to trouble during their weekly chats on the telephone. Her mother had always been inclined to be vague and latterly even more so, but that could be due to age. Still pretty, still winsome, she had over the years clung like clematis around her sturdy oak of a husband, relying utterly upon his decisiveness, trusting completely in his judgment, blossoming so much in his care that she was able occasionally to indulge in the small vanity of assuring passing customers: 'I'm sixty-five years old, you know!' then preening as they voiced genuine disbelief.

Music from a transistor drowned Dove's entry into the flat. She traced the sound to the kitchen and stood for a moment in the doorway watching her mother's unusually slow movements as she prepared vegetables for lunch. Dove's frown deepened as she recalled watching her mother preparing Christmas dinner last time she was home, the way her nimble fingers had stripped sprouts of their outer leaves, had diced carrots and crumbled bread for stuffing, then how, when a favourite tune had been played on the radio, she had swung gaily from the sink to demonstrate the intricate steps of an old tyme dance—a pastime to which both parents were addicted.

'Mother!' Dove spoke loudly to combat the sound of music.

The knife clattered from her mother's hand as she

swung from the sink. 'Dove,' she gasped, slumping against the unit, 'how you startled me!'

Dove hurried to slip a supporting arm around her mother's waist. 'I'm sorry, I didn't mean to frighten you. Sit down, you look quite ashen.' She scanned her face while levering her into a chair, wondering with quick concern how it was possible for a person to age ten years in a matter of months. Retaining her shaking hands in her own warm clasp, she pulled forward a stool and sat down opposite. Gently she reproved, 'Mother, you've obviously not been well. Why wasn't I told?—you know I would have come home immediately had I had the least inkling.'

Her mother's eyes brightened. Lifting a hand to Dove's head, she smoothed her fingers over silken strands of hair. 'Silver in moonlight, gold in the sun,' she murmured inconsequentially. 'I know you would have come home, child, but the need has never arisen. I can't imagine why you should think I've been ill.'

'Now, Mother!' Dove's tone was gently determined. 'Something is wrong, I'm convinced of it. Are you going to tell me without a struggle or must I prise it out of you?'

'You're so clever at that, my darling,' her mother sighed, 'gently intimidating, quite as determined as your father, though without his autocratic manner which some misguided people regard as arrogance. Why can't others see him as we do?' She gulped. 'Why can't these petty officials who pester us acknowledge that a man who for years was an Army major can't be expected to tolerate any infringement upon his liberty, nor to allow any interference in his private affairs? Now that he's a civilian he's entitled to run his own life in his own way.' Bright spots of colour appeared in her cheeks, as rather shrilly she spilled out her indignation. 'Life in married quarters was no picnic, as some people were inclined to think. Granted, we Army wives had the excitement of travel, the satisfaction of being close to our husbands, and a comradeship unequalled in civilian life, yet we were bound always by irksome rules which, for the good of the community, had to be upheld, and for twenty years we put up with them. But now circumstances are very different. As your father quite rightly pointed out, he's no longer bound by regulations, he's entitled to make his own decisions and to run his business in any way he thinks fit.'

As her mother's spate of words threatened to escalate into a torrent, Dove held out a delaying hand. 'One moment, Mother,' she interrupted, feeling a stirring of dismay. 'Who's Father been crossing swords with? Not the Inland Revenue inspector *again*!'

The question was answered when her mother rose to her feet, erect and bridling. 'Who else?' She looked fiercely ready to defend her absent husband from criticism, however gentle. 'Isn't he the one who persistently hounds him for money he doesn't possess? Who's harassed and worried him to such an extent that he no longer has any appetite? I needn't remind you how much your father enjoyed his food, yet for three whole days now he's eaten no more than a couple of crackers and a tiny piece of cheese. Oh, Dove ...!' Suddenly the fight went out of her and she collapsed into a chair, covered her face with her hands and began sobbing. 'I'm so worried about your father, darling, thank God you've come home! Perhaps you'll be able to find a solution—we're both of us too old to be worried in this way. At our age we need peace and contentment, not this dreadful, never-ending strife!'

Thankful that her father was being kept occupied in the shop below, Dove set about consoling her mother, and after numerous cups of tea and assurances—given with fingers crossed—that she would personally see to it that matters were straightened out, she finally persuaded her to continue with her preparations for lunch, so that when at precisely twelve-thirty, not a second earlier nor later, her father practised his habitual custom of reversing the Open sign on the door to show Closed, pulled down the blind and turned the key firmly in the lock, lunch would be ready to serve and the hour's break he allowed himself would not be wasted. She would need to probe, she realised, deeply and carefully as a surgeon with a scalpel, until she unearthed all the relative information about his financial position. He would resent her questioning, would pooh-pooh the idea that she, a mere slip of a girl, could resolve a situation he seemingly could not. Donald Grey expected of his womenfolk only that they be decorative and indulge in gentle feminine pursuits. 'Measure a man by his stand at time of challenge', he had often stated, secure in the knowledge that he had never been found wanting. Great tact would be needed if his burden were to be eased without sacrifice to his pride.

The table was laid and lunch ready to be served when Donald Grey stomped up the stairs and into the flat. For a moment, since he was unaware of Dove's presence, his stature and expression epitomised depression. Never had she seen his upright, soldierly figure so stooped, his elderly handsome face so ravaged with worry. With eyebrows beetling beneath a thatch of thick grey hair, he glanced around the room, then spotted Dove, who was waiting, slightly smiling, to be noticed.

'Dove, sweetheart! When did you arrive? Why didn't you tell me she was here?' he reproved his wife. 'Wanted to keep her all to yourself, eh?'

'Of course not, Donald,' she laughed, delighted that Dove's presence had brought back the sparkle to his eyes and a return of the teasing banter she loved. 'She arrived a bare half hour ago, I haven't had the opportunity even to ask her whether this is a flying visit or a break between jobs. Let's all sit down at the table, shall we? We can talk after we've eaten.'

Whether from genuine hunger or simply to allay suspicion, Mr Grey ate a hearty meal, then, replete and seemingly contented, he pushed away his plate, leant back in his chair, then instructed his daughter fondly, 'Now, young woman, I want to hear all your news, how your employer has been treating you and how you've managed with your current crop of babies.'

He waited, his eyes upon her face, and was rewarded by a sight that always delighted him, a rogue dimple that appeared at the corner of her mouth whenever she smiled.

'My late employer was one of the very best,' Dove supplied, 'and as for the infants, they're now aboard ship with their mother, who's decided she can no longer bear to be separated from her husband, so she's gone to Iran to join him.'

'So wise of her,' her mother nodded approval. 'A wife's place is by her husband's side, wherever his job may take him, and children, provided they're healthy, will thrive in any climate and under any conditions. It often irked me, my dear,' she sighed, 'that you had to be left in England while your father and I were abroad, but you were never a robust child and as our doctor was so adamantly against your going with us to Lagos, where your father was posted when you were five years old, we had no choice but to leave you at boarding school.'

Dove frowned. As usual, whenever this subject was mentioned, her mother sounded apologetic, even guilty. 'I understand, Mother,' she reassured her. 'I enjoyed my years at boarding school.'

'Well then,' her father interrupted, 'what happens now?'

She shrugged. 'I get another job.'

'As easily as that?' he laughed. 'Aren't you being rather a conceited puss?'

'Not really,' she answered. 'As it happens, the popularity of the job I've been trained to do has hit an all-time low. Very few girls, it seems, wish to take up child nursing, and while one might imagine that the practice of employing nannies has waned, the reverse is actually the case. Demand far exceeds the supply.'

Looking obviously gratified, her mother stood up and began gathering up the plates. 'Such a fitting occupation for a young woman, I've always thought. Your father and I spent many hours deliberating upon which profession would be most suitable for a girl of your cloistered upbringing, and I must say we're delighted with our choice. So refined, so genteel....'

Dove winced from the description. 'It's hardly that, Mother! Today's children are very advanced, some are appalling little horrors—you'd never believe some of the remarks I've heard passed in the nursery! But enough about me, I want to hear all your news.' She turned her attention upon her father. 'Tell me, how is business?'

His face clouded. Glancing quickly at his watch, he rose as if to leave, but his wife forestalled him. Hurriedly, conscious of imminent argument, she offered, 'I'll open up the shop while you stay and chat to Dove,' then she whipped off her apron and almost ran out of the flat, leaving Dove alone with her surprised, a trifle resentful father.

Deciding that to skirt around the subject would be a waste of time, she grabbed it by the neck by demanding in a calm, determined manner, 'How much do you owe the tax people, Father, and why hasn't it been paid?'

A shadow of hauteur crossed his features as he treated her to the sort of look an officer might bestow upon a dissident subordinate. But when her steady grey gaze did not falter he slumped against the back of his chair, a weary soldier, grey with battle fatigue. 'The money hasn't been paid because I refused from the very beginning to submit to becoming an unpaid tax collector on behalf of the Government. This value added tax is iniquitous, the amount of work entailed is a diabolical infringment of the small amount of spare time left to a man once the business of the day is done. Do you know,' he shot up straight, blue eyes glaring, 'that when the tax was first imposed they actually had the effrontery to send round an official who was supposed to show me how to keep my own books! Naturally I sent him away with a flea in his ear.'

He snorted. 'Never in my life have I asked help of anyone, and all I want is to be left alone to run my business, to provide for myself and your mother. Neither of us hanker after luxuries—having travelled extensively we have no wish to holiday abroad, no desire for a car, no inclination to dine in expensive restaurants, so our needs are very simple and we've managed very nicely with the income from the shop. We were enjoying a comfortable existence until January of this year when the first of the officials from the Inland Revenue paid us a visit demanding arrears of tax which he insisted ought to have been paid in previous years. I ordered him out, of course, but persistently he returned to harass, to question, to demand. My mind was reduced to such a state of turmoil I found myself unable to concentrate upon the shop—it's become badly neglected, as you'll no doubt see for yourself— but the amount of money demanded was so exorbitant I felt certain I was the victim of some official blunder. Then last week I received this letter.' From his inner pocket he withdrew a well-thumbed sheet of paper and silently handed it to Dove. She unfolded it, glanced at the official crest dominating the page, then read its stilted, typewritten message.

Colour drained from her face before she had finished reading. It was worse than she had steeled herself to expect. Disjointed sentences jumped out of the written page—lack of co-operation; unwillingness to accept guidance; adamant refusal to settle outstanding debt; no alternative but to put matters in the hands of the Official Receiver!

'Am I right in suspecting,' her father's usually reson-ant voice quavered like a child's, 'that our home and business will be put up for sale in order so that they can recover the amount they insist I owe them?'

Dove drew in a shuddering breath. 'It won't be allowed to come to that, Father,' she choked, 'it *mustn't* be! I'll visit the office myself, offer to pay off the debt in small instalments,' she carried on eagerly, half of her mind juggling with finances, calculating what amount could be spared out of her salary. Already she had amassed a small nest-egg by saving a regular amount each month. With a living-in job expenses could be trimmed to a minimum, so she could quite easily afford to double the amount she was already saving.

Relaxing a little, she sent her father a reassuring smile. 'Don't worry, darling, between us we'll clear off the debt in no time. How much is it, by the way?'

His answer had the effect of a vicious hand clutching her throat and squeezing hard. 'How ... how much did you say?' Smoke-grey eyes pleading to be told he had just indulged in some sort of macabre joke.

'Four thousand pounds,' was his heavy, despairing reply. 'That's the amount I must find if your mother and I are not to be left homeless and without means of support.'

Dove's spirits zoomed to zero. How on earth could a children's nurse be expected to raise such a huge amount? With the best will in the world, a well-paid job, and practising stringent economies, it would still take the better part of ten years to accumulate all that money. *Unless* ...! She was almost afraid to ponder further, but tentatively she forced herself to recall some of the stories Jennifer Pedder, a close friend since schooldays, had recounted about the vast sums of money being offered to English girls working in the Arab States. The information was first-hand because Jennifer, herself an air hostess, had been the recipient of lavish tips from generous oil sheikh passengers. Other hostesses, Jennifer had assured her, who had been dated by wealthy young Arabs had fared even better—one girl had received a three-thousand-pound bracelet simply for allowing herself to be escorted to one of the world's finest restaurants, eating a delicious dinner, and lending an attentive ear to her Arab host's troubles.

'A three-thousand-pound bracelet just for that!' Dove had queried suspiciously.

'So she said,' Jennifer had shrugged, 'and having seen for myself the way these oil sheikhs throw their money about I find it hard not to believe her.'

'Daddy,' Dove swallowed hard, 'do you know if Jennifer Pedder is home?'

'What ...? Er—who ...?' He had been so deep in thought she had to repeat the question. 'Oh, that school friend of yours! Yes, I often see her about—I was talking to her only last week. She's based at London Airport, I believe, so as that's a mere thirty miles away I expect she comes home pretty frequently. Why not phone her home and ask?'

'I'll do that!' Dove reached a sudden decision.

'Don't worry, Daddy,' she stopped in passing to run consoling fingers through his hair. 'Go downstairs and give Mummy a hand in the shop—no sense in your brooding alone up here.' She hesitated, then continued cautiously. 'I don't want to say too much at this stage in case I should raise false hopes, but I think I may have found a solution to our problem. Nothing definite as yet,' she added hastily when his head jerked up, 'just a barely formed idea shimmering, as it were, upon the horizon.'

Jennifer was home and delighted to hear from her. 'Come over!' she pressed. 'I'm sunbathing in the garden, we can have a lovely long natter.'

As the Pedder house was less than a mile away, ten minutes later Dove had parked her car in the drive and was making her way along a side path leading into a secluded garden enclosed on three sides by trees and colourful shrubs with, in its centre, a circular lawn where Dove discovered her bikini-clad friend stretched out on one of two loungers placed strategically to catch the maximum amount of sunshine.

'This is great!' Jennifer sat upright at Dove's approach. 'For once, our visits home have coincided. How vexed I've been on previous visits to discover either that you'd been home the previous week or that you were expected a couple of days after I was due to leave. How long is it since we last met? A year ...?'

'It must be all of that.' Dove smiled as she eased the vacant lounger beneath the shade of a tree. 'I can't sit in the sun, it makes me sick,' she explained in response to Jennifer's raised eyebrows.

'Poor you!' Jennifer stretched like a contented kitten. 'I love it, which is just as well considering the amount of time I spend in warm climates.'

'I know. That's why I'm here, I want some advice.'

'From me?' Jennifer's russet hair almost stood on end. 'Cool, competent Dove seeking advice from a scatterbrain like me?'

'You're not the scatterbrain you'd have people believe,' Dove replied with the straightforwardness of an old friend. 'You act out the pose very convincingly, but it's never fooled me.'

'All right,' Jennifer's freckled face creased into a grin, 'so underneath I'm really a hard-headed bitch, experienced in the ways of the sinful world. Having got that sorted out, how can I help?'

'You're not any of those things either.' When Dove's serious expression did not lift Jennifer realized that her friend was in no mood for frivolity, so she sat upright and with matching gravity demanded to know,

'What's troubling you?'

The fact that Dove seemed to find difficulty in choosing her words caused Jennifer even more concern. They had been friends since childhood, had been inseparable at boarding school, had shared adolescent doubts and fears. Never, until now, had either of them found it hard to exchange confidences.

'Were those tales you told about English girls making their fortunes in the East really true?' The question trickling from Dove's lips became the prelude to a flood. Giving Jennifer no time to reply she rushed on, 'I'm in desperate need of a lot of money—four thousand pounds, to be exact—but I've no hope whatsoever of earning that much in this country. Then I remem-

bered your tales about the rich Arabs and how well
they treated their employees. I'm between jobs at the
moment, so if you can advise me how to go about it, I
might manage to get a job out East. Without wishing
to sound conceited, I can confirm that a British nanny
is a highly prized commodity, and that being so, I'd
like to cash in on my assets. Trouble is, I don't know
where to start.'

Jennifer expelled her pent-up breath, then stared at
her friend, speechless with shock. She had no need to
ask why Dove was in such desperate need of money;
the small village community in which they lived had
been buzzing for weeks with rumours of Donald Grey's
impending bankruptcy. Her father, an accountant, had
been scathing and, Jennifer thought, unusually unsym-
pathetic. 'Any man who tries to set himself above the
law of the land is a fool,' he had replied to Jennifer's
troubled query. 'Granted, we're all inclined to rant and
rave about the unfairness of our tax system, nevertheless, most of us pay up in the end. Not Donald Grey,
however. No, in his usual autocratic manner he decided
to take on the might of a Government department
single-handed, and not surprisingly has come off worst.
The man is way past retirement age, either he ought to
sell the business or employ a manager, one young
enough to cope with the complications and stress in-
herent in modern business procedure.' Unaware of the
seriousness of the situation, Jennifer had pushed the
matter to the back of her mind, hardly associating it
with her friend, but now she was having to frantically
marshal her thoughts in order to put forward a cool,
calm argument that would convince Dove that the

drastic step she was contemplating was simply not on.

Her voice was calm, yet her eyes mirrored dismay as she affirmed, 'The tales I told you were true enough. Desert sheikhs and millionaire business tycoons are flocking to London in search of young English girls with special qualifications, and they pay well for their services. Four thousand a year isn't unusual, so I'm told.' She sensed Dove making rapid calculations. 'Also they provide luxurious rent-free apartments within their palaces. Some girls have reputedly been supplied with their own personal servants and also ... *armed bodyguards*!' Watching Dove closely, she drove home her point when her friend's grey eyes widened with alarm. 'Yes, it's not all caviar and honey! There's a lot of political unrest in the Arab States, a prince can be deposed almost overnight, and when he is his entire household is at grave risk—even his children's English nanny! So dismiss the idea completely, Dove, it's most certainly not for you.'

'But why not?' Dove's voice was implacable. 'If other English girls are prepared to face the risks why shouldn't I?'

For the first time since the conversation began Jennifer permitted herself a smile. 'Because you're ... just you, I suppose.'

'Would you elaborate upon that remark?' Dove asked with asperity. 'I'm healthy, unmarried, and over twenty-one, I'm also a highly qualified children's nurse —so why do you imply that I'm unsuitable?'

Jennifer was left with no alternative but to be brutal. Swinging her legs off the lounger, she faced Dove to spell out with implicit frankness, 'I'll tell you why. I've become friendly with some of the girls who have taken on such jobs, have talked with them, have wondered at the danger they face and their utter disregard for their own safety. Super-cool, some are trained to shoot, others could snap off an arm without the slightest compunction—and such an act can become necessary, Dove, because for a girl to be on her own in the Middle East she has to be prepared for anything—even to kill.

'Now, in complete contrast,' she went on, 'consider yourself. An only child born to middle-aged parents whose idea of bringing up a child was to treat her like a doll, to dress her up, to invite admiration, but never allow her to be touched. Then at five years old, to dump her in a boarding school run by middle-aged spinster daughters of ex-Army officers, themselves so cloistered and out of touch with reality they might have been beings from another planet. Even though you were allowed to spend holidays at my home, I always sensed your parents' faint disapproval at my frivolous ways. Their scandalised expressions when I told them of my decision to become an air hostess was proof enough that they thought my parents far too lenient. *You* would have loved to have become an air hostess, wouldn't you, Dove?' she challenged fiercely. 'Come on now, admit it, the only reason you're a children's nurse is because you wouldn't upset your parents by going against their wishes! So you followed their dictates, and in consequence you've remained as naïve as the children you spend your life with. So there rests my case!' She jumped up to glare defiance at Dove. 'If I've offended you, I'm sorry, but for your own sake it had to be said.'

'Oh, do sit down and stop playing to the gallery.' Dove's easy reply had more effect than any outburst. Feeling slightly foolish, Jennifer sank down upon her knees and began moodily plucking blades of grass.

'Are you very angry with me?' she asked soberly.

'Not a scrap,' Dove chuckled. 'I agree with every word.'

'Then you'll drop the whole foolish idea?'

'Jennifer, will you please keep quiet long enough to listen to my point of view? Here am I, as you so rightly pointed out, twenty-one years of age and a complete innocent so far as the realities of life are concerned. So can you blame me for wanting to be free of my dull rut, to take part in life instead of continuing as a mere spectator? Yes, even if it brings me strife and regret, even danger, at least I'll be living and not just existing from day to boring day! I've been thinking along these lines for quite some time now, but I haven't mustered sufficient courage to take the necessary steps towards change. Now, however, circumstances have made it difficult for me to do otherwise. But I'm not being forced against my will, this is something I really *want* to do! Now, will you help me or must I take the long way round and search out the facts for myself?'

Jennifer's amazement was great; it was quite some time before she could voice her surprise, her unwilling admiration. 'You dared to imply that I adopted a pose!' she gasped. 'What about yourself? Even I was not aware that your demure exterior was a cover for seething discontent. You actually have more spunk than I have!' she laughed, then sobered. 'However, I still think you're being foolhardy. If it weren't for the possibility that you might end up in the hands of some sleazy agency I wouldn't consider advising you, as it is I will give you the address of one I know to be strictly above board. If you can satisfy their very stringent requirements and they agree to fix you up with a job then my conscience will be clear.' She jumped to her feet, still agitated by her friend's decision yet feeling compelled to help her. 'I'll nip into the house now, before I have time to weaken, and get you the address.'

# CHAPTER TWO

THE office of the Chatsworth Nannies Agency was situated in a tiny street in London's West End. Dove halted when she recognised the name-plate and wavered at the foot of a flight of stairs, her eyes fixed upon a painted arrow pointing upwards towards her destination. She was fifteen minutes early for her appointment. Should she go up, or linger in the street for a further ten minutes? A gust of wind whipping around her ankles made the decision easier and she began the ascent with unhurried grace and a confidence born not of conceit but of a certain knowledge that she was good at her job, a fact easily established by the wad of reference tucked into her handbag. Nevertheless, her heart reacted with quick nervous bumps as she approached the agency's glass-plated door which represented entry into a completely different world, a world of travel, of strange exciting places, unusual customs, alien tongues.

A young receptionist looked up from her typewriter and smiled enquiringly as Dove entered the office.

'I'm Dove Grey,' she forced an even tenor into a voice threatening to tremble with excitement. 'My appointment isn't for another fifteen minutes, but as it's so cold outside I wondered if you would mind my waiting inside?'

'Of course not, Miss Grey,' the girl jumped to her

feet, 'please take a seat.' She waved towards a plush-looking chair upholstered in bright red leather. 'I'll tell Mrs Todd you've arrived, but I know she won't be able to see you immediately as she is expecting another client.' She glanced down at her watch and frowned. 'He's already five minutes late. But while you're waiting can I get you something—a coffee, perhaps?'

'A coffee would be lovely,' Dove nodded gratefully, and relaxed into the proffered chair looking, in her neat grey coat and white knitted beret, completely unperturbed even though her pulse rate was averaging umpteen thumps a minute.

She was just about to swallow her first mouthful of coffee when the outer door was flung open and a man erupted into the room on a gust of chilling wind. As he strode past without sparing her a glance Dove shivered in his draught. He paused momentarily outside of the door of the inner office, sparing no words on the young receptionist but merely hooking a fierce eyebrow which startled from her the jerky response,

'Please go straight in, Monsieur Blais, Mrs Todd is expecting you.'

When the door closed behind his tall frame the young girl slumped back in her chair, then, with a candour born of inexperience, confided to the wide-eyed Dove, 'Poor Mrs Todd, she's been keyed up for a fortnight worrying about this meeting, ever since she received his letter requesting—no, demanding—an appointment. He's our most difficult client,' she continued without encouragement from Dove. 'Not one of the half dozen nannies we've sent him has lasted more than a month in his employment.'

'Really?' Dove's response was cool and the girl sensing her disapproval, blushed and without further comment resumed her typing.

Dove suppressed a smile. The youngster was obviously huffed by the slight snub, yet if she were to make any progress in her chosen career the sooner she learnt about discretion and loyalty the better. And yet she could not help but feel a sneaking sympathy for the girl whose body had jerked with fright the moment that black-frowning tornado had gusted into the office. She had not had time to distinguish his features, but his movements as he had swept past had stamped indelibly upon her mind an impression of suppressed impatience, of an intolerant nature resentful of trivial demands upon its time. And there had been one other thing she could not quite pinpoint—an aura of fury, perhaps, such as might be projected by a bird of the wild trapped momentarily inside a cage.

At the sound of raised voices Dove's eyes lifted from the page of the magazine she had been scanning without interest and remained riveted upon the tall dark shadow outlined against the glass door of the inner office. She watched the outline of a black-clad arm reaching out for the door knob, then, when the door was a few inches ajar, saw the arm fall away as its owner resumed a scathing attack upon the unseen, unfortunate Mrs Todd.

'I came here, madame,' his cold incisive tone cut through the silence of both rooms, 'because I was assured you ran the most efficient agency in the country. Six times you have proved my informant wrong! Six times you have supplied me with inept, spineless, in-

competent samples of womanhood. Not one of the six
was capable of self-motivated thought, not one would I
have trusted to take charge of a mongrel puppy, much
less two high-spirited, intelligent children! And now,
madame, you add insult to aggravation by suggesting
that the fault lies not with your staff but within the
household where they have been employed. I wonder,'
his voice slated with sarcasm, 'where you find the
temerity to make such remarks!'

'The reason is simple, monsieur, it is that I have
never found it difficult to speak the truth.'

Dove checked an impulse to applaud when the unseen woman proffered the unruffled, even-tempered reply. She obviously had no intention of crumbling under
the pressure being applied with such arrogance. 'Over
a period of eighteen months,' the woman continued,
'you've reduced six of my best employees to tearful
mental wrecks, and I have no intention of allowing you
to do the same to a seventh. My girls,' one could almost
sense her swell of pride, 'are the most sought-after on
earth. The world's wealthy are beating a path to my
door in search of a new generation of highly-skilled,
level-headed young nannies to bring up tomorrow's
princes, statesmen and giants of industry. Only here in
Britain do they find what they seek, girls of sterling
character, of high principles, girls of such rare integrity
they are almost unique. At random, without referring
to my files, I can recall an employee who was given a
gold watch worth two thousand pounds by a grateful
employer. Another was flown to London first class when
she became ill, was put up in a penthouse suite at the
Dorchester and received treatment from a top specialist.

My girls are so prized they are treated like princesses, they travel in private jets, stay at Claridges in London, the Crillon in Paris, and the Baur au Lac in Zürich. At this very moment I have clients of great wealth and esteem waiting patiently for the services of one of my nannies, an oil tycoon in Texas, a world motor racing champion in Switzerland, a European prince, even one of our own ambassadors here in London. I admit that you pay a generous salary, monsieur, probably the highest of any of my clients, but not for twice that amount would I permit another of my girls to enter your employment!'

Feeling a sense of partisanship with the courageous Mrs Todd, Dove waited, expecting to see a vanquished male slinking out of the office. Then his hard reply fell upon her ears and it became obvious that the man was too insensitive to even recognise censure.

'You have, unwittingly perhaps, put your finger right on the canker eating away at the foundations of your organisation. Your employees have become corrupted by greed. They come out East expecting to encounter sheikhs with the looks of a film star riding in from the desert on snow-white stallions. Once they discover that the majority of Arabs drive around in air-conditioned Cadillacs and are totally uninterested in Western women their enthusiasm wanes and petulance shows its sulky face. I say good riddance to your sex-starved, money-grabbing British nannies, Madame Todd; in future I shall be guided by my own judgement which tells me to employ a sensible, intelligent Frenchwoman.'

With lips clamped tight he spun on his heel and strode towards the exit, casting a look of distaste upon each of them as he passed, a look so contemptuous, so denigrating, it aroused within them a state of furious resentment, the furore of a dovecote whose inhabitants' feathers have been ruffled by a savagely pecking hawk.

For a second after the door banged shut behind him they were speechless, their faces registering various degrees of anger, consternation and, in Dove's case, downright shock. Then the young girl exploded.

'Who does he think he is ...!'

The question jerked a response from the svelte, businesslike woman sagging in a seemingly uncharacteristic attitude on the threshold of her office. Making a visible effort to pull herself together, she straightened and rebuked briskly:

'That's enough of that, Sandra.' Then with a look of apology she turned to Dove. 'I'm sorry you had to witness such a scene, Miss Grey, it must have left you with a very bad impression. I assure you, however, that what you've just heard is not the usual reaction we receive from our clients. Please,' she stepped to one side, still shaken, 'come into my office and we'll find out if we can be of help to one another.'

By the time she had ushered Dove into her office and taken her seat behind a desk littered with several piles of correspondence she seemed calmer; only her expertly-tinted hair, slightly disarranged by agitated fingers, gave a clue to the trauma so recently experienced.

'Now, Miss Grey,' she rustled through a pile of papers in search of Dove's application, 'from information contained in your letter I gather you have all the qualifications we seek—and more.' She shot a look of encouragement across the width of the desk, but her smile faded when she noted Dove's pinched features, the grey eyes wide with shock. 'My dear,' she half-rose, then changed her mind and resumed her seat, 'that distasteful scene has upset you more than I'd imagined. Are you wondering if all my clients are like Monsieur Blais?' Her tone went dry. 'Believe me, if they were I would close up shop this very minute!'

Dove had to smile. 'I'm not shocked, Mrs Todd, just startled. I hate rows ...' she trailed off, wondering herself why the actions of a complete stranger should have affected her so adversely. Schooldays spent in the company of girls whose Army background had instilled into them instant obedience, the serene tenor of her own homelife, and the ultra-civilised households in which she had worked had rendered her a total stranger to violent abuse. No wonder her hands and knees were shaking, her mouth dry with fear. The man had reacted like a barbarian—a species she had thought extinct!

'I agree,' Mrs Todd nodded, 'rows are not pleasant, but to be quite fair to Monsieur Blais I feel I must explain a little of his background. Perhaps then you may feel able to make allowances.'

'*Allowances?* You mean you're able to excuse ...'

'As I'm sure you will, too, my dear, if only you'll give me time to explain.' Dove's shrug indicated that she would be wasting her time, nevertheless Mrs Todd went on firmly, 'The most frequent complaint I've received about that man is that he's too strict a disciplinarian, yet this quality, among many others, is essential to the success of the very important, potentially dangerous job he has elected to do—that of ensuring the

safety of a family with, as its head, one of the richest
men in the world.' Catching the sound of Dove's
startled gasp, she smiled. 'Ah, I thought that would
make you sit up and take notice! Sheikh Rahma bin
Jabir is head of one of the most noble and respected
families in Neffe, a country which, since the discovery
of oil, has become the richest place for its size on earth.
However, just as in suburbia, or indeed any stratum of
society, one person's good fortune gives rise to jealousy
in his neighbours. Such is the state in Neffe. It's become an inflammable corner of the world, where assas-
sination plots are commonplace, where sheikh turns
upon sheikh and even brother upon brother. So you see,
Monsieur Blais hasn't the most enviable job in the
world.' Tiring of the subject, she reached for Dove's
application form. 'I consider we've wasted quite enough
time on that gentleman this morning, let's get on with
the matter of finding you a suitable situation.'

It took great effort to clear her mind of Monsieur
Blais's exotic life and to concentrate upon her own
mundane affairs, but as Mrs Todd began shooting questions across the desk Dove gathered her wits and made
her replies equally concise and businesslike. After fifteen minutes' intensive grilling, Mrs Todd asked to see
her references and after thorough scrutiny allowed her
lips to relax into a pleased smile.

'I shall need to go through the usual formality of
checking these, of course,' she tapped the letters with a
thumbnail, 'but once that's been done I shall have no
difficulty whatsoever in placing you in a satisfactory
situation. Sir Joshua Arcourt, for example,' once again
she rummaged through the letters on her desk, 'has

pestered me for weeks to find him a suitable nanny. How would you like to work for one of our country's foremost ambassadors?'

'Oh, but ...' Belatedly Dove remembered the most vital stipulation. 'I want to work abroad, preferably in the Middle East.'

Mrs Todd looked stunned and seemed incapable for a second of finding words. 'The Middle East? *You* ...? My dear child, are you sure you know all that such a job would entail?'

'Probably not,' Dove admitted, then went on firmly, 'nevertheless, that's where I want to go.'

'But why? With your qualifications I could let you take your pick of half a dozen plum jobs right here in this country.'

Dove's chin thrust stubbornly. 'If I'd wanted to stay in this country,' she explained carefully, not wanting to sound bigheaded, 'I wouldn't have needed to come to you nor to any other agency. You see, I too have a waiting list of people, all very well connected—even some minor royalty—who've begged me to work for them. But for personal reasons I want to work abroad.'

'I take it that for "personal reasons" I can read *money*?' Mrs Todd enquired dryly.

'That among other things,' Dove admitted, feeling a humiliated blush staining her cheeks.

A shade of disappointment crossed the older woman's face. She began gathering up papers and secured them with a wire clip. 'In that case, Miss Grey,' her tone was one of finality, 'I'm afraid we've both been wasting our time. I'm sorry, but there's nothing I can do to help you.'

Dove got to her feet. 'Nothing ...? But why? You admit to having many vacancies on your books and say that you're short of well trained nannies, so why ...?'

'Sit down and I'll tell you why.' Grimly Mrs Todd waited until Dove obeyed. 'I may give an impression of being hard and very much the business woman, and perhaps to a certain extent I am, but I refuse to suffer months of agonised conscience on your behalf—which is what would be in store for me were I to send an innocent such as yourself abroad. Wait!' she commanded when Dove tried to argue. 'Even had I not seen with my own eyes the havoc wreaked upon your nerves by a man's Middle Eastern manners, instinct alone would have sufficed to warn me not to fall in with your request. As it is, Miss Grey, I've seen you reduced to a quaking jelly by words *not even intended for you.* Mark my words, Monsieur Blais is typical, not unique. Arabs—and if it's money you're after you've no doubt set your sights upon a job in one of the Arab States— have an unnerving contempt for women. You'll probably find it difficult to believe, but among the older generation of Arabs especially, any man without sons is pitied for being childless—no matter how many daughters he may have.'

Dove tried to hide the nervous tremor in her voice as she countered, 'Other girls have managed to overcome such obstacles, so why shouldn't I? I'm not on the lookout for a husband, merely a job.'

'Then you won't get any help from me.' Purposefully Mrs Todd rose to her feet and walked around the desk. Almost sadly she held out her hand. 'Goodbye, Miss Grey. If ever you should change your mind please con-

tact me. But if, heaven forbid, you should decide to continue with such folly then all I can do is wish you good
luck—you'll certainly need it!'

Dove strode into the outer office with her head held
high. In many ways Mrs Todd had been kind, but such
an abrupt dismissal had left her feeling humiliated.
With much interest the young receptionist noted flags
of colour flying high in Dove's cheeks and her sympathy was obvious as she consoled,

'Gave you a rough time, did she? Never mind, there
are other agencies. If at first you don't succeed ...
that's what I always say.' Seemingly unaware that her
conversation consisted entirely of platitudes, she aired
yet another. 'Count your blessings as I do! So you have
no job. But at least you haven't an employer like Monsieur Blais either! I feel sorry for anyone forced to
work for a man like him. I don't mind betting that even
the staff at the Dorchester will heave a sigh of relief
when the time comes for him to leave.'

Dove thanked her for her condolences and left the
office to stumble her way downstairs. When she reached
the pavement she hesitated, wondering which direction to choose. Her train was not due to leave for hours
yet. She had planned, once she had the promise of a job,
to spend the rest of the day shopping for clothes suitable for a Middle Eastern climate, but now even
window-shopping held no appeal. She felt depressed,
weary and chilled to the bone.

*Count your blessings*, the young receptionist had
said. What blessings? Would she have been so blithely
unconcerned if she faced the prospect of seeing her
elderly parents turned out of their home, deprived of

their livelihood, unless she could find a job well paid enough to ease the financial mess?

'Oh, blast!' she muttered into her collar as she faced an icy wind. 'Why couldn't I have pulled it off? I didn't realise until now how much I'd been looking forward to a change of scenery, a change of climate, away from this temperamental spring weather—one day basking in sunshine and the next freezing cold. I do believe I'd even be tempted to work for that tyrannical Frenchman . . .' She stopped so abruptly that a man following behind cannoned into her.

'So sorry . . .'

'Oh, no, it was my fault, really,' she stammered when with gentlemanly concern he tried to accept the blame.

He continued on his way with a smile, wishing he were thirty years younger so that he, too, might share some of the optimism, the surging hope, he had seen reflected in the face of a lovely young girl.

# CHAPTER THREE

IT was not until after Dove had hailed a taxi, told the driver her destination, then collapsed into the back seat, that she began feeling shivers of apprehension.

'Well, why not?' She hugged herself fiercely. 'It's worth a try—he wants a nanny and I want a job! The worst he can do is have me thrown out.'

The taxi took an interminable time to weave a way through traffic jams, yet when they drew up outside the Dorchester it seemed mere foolhardy seconds since the plan had formulated in her mind. Forcing herself not to weaken, she paid off the taxi driver, marched into the hotel and went straight to the reception desk.

'I should like to see Monsieur Blais, please,' she told the young man behind the desk.

'Is he expecting you?' he asked, showing a kindling of interest as his gaze lit upon the small pointed face and grey eyes made enormous by either trepidation or excitement.

'No,' she admitted reluctantly. Then with a flash of inspiration, 'But if you tell him I'm from the Chatsworth Nannies Agency I'm sure he'll see me.'

The young man lost interest. With such a face and figure he had imagined her to be a model at the very least!

'Very well, I'll tell him you're here.'

Dove was not certain whether her stomach was misbehaving because of nerves or whether it was simply the effect of the silently moving lift bearing her upwards towards a penthouse suite on the top floor.

'Some of the oil shiekhs' money must have rubbed off on Monsieur Blais,' she muttered, swallowing back a nervous giggle as she dithered on the threshold of the room at present occupied by the formidable Frenchman. Then taking a deep, steadying breath she rapped hard on the door, straining her ears lest she should miss what she imagined would be a terse command to enter.

She was standing with her head forward, one anxious ear almost pressed against the door panel, when the door opened suddenly and she all but overbalanced into the room. Feeling exceedingly foolish, she straightened and with an apology on her lips traced upwards with her eyes along a length of richly patterned red silk dressing gown in search of the face towering somewhere up above.

'Who are you?' The question came sharp as a shot from a rifle and as her eyes finally found his face its impact upon her senses was equally vital. All she remembered of the man was that he had a tall frame with military bearing and a stern, clipped voice. If she had seen his face she would not have come, never would have summoned up sufficient nerve to face features dark and sharply etched as the desert hawk; eyes of steel grey, and a rock-hard mouth tugged down at one corner into a permanent sneer by a puckered scar slicing deep from lip to chin.

'I ... I ...' Her throat seized up with fear.

The black hawk-head swooped to peer into her face. 'Do I know you, mademoiselle? Ah yes, I believe I do!' He snapped his fingers, causing her to jump. 'Did I not see you in the agency less than an hour ago? So Madame Todd has relented! I knew she would—you British will do anything for money! Don't stand there dithering, come inside, we have much to discuss!'

s he ushered her impatiently inside Dove managed a quick look around the apartment, noting letters that had cascaded from a pile jumbled on top of a writing desk and were now strewing the floor, an open brief-case bulging with correspondence, a half-filled coffee cup pushed to one side of a small table as if its recipient had found the contents disgusting. His suit jacket hung precariously over the back of a chair, but he made no effort to retrieve it, nor did he apologise for his casual attire. She stiffened with apprehension when he waved her towards a chair. The room and its occupant had an atmosphere of frustrated ill-temper, a suspicion that was borne out by his cold, clipped tone as he addressed her.

'No doubt Mrs Todd has supplied you with all the relevant details, but at the risk of sounding repetitious I prefer that you hear them from me. All too often in the past I have heard remonstrances from nannies who vowed they had no idea what they were letting them-selves in for when they agreed to work in Neffe. I wish to ensure that you are under no misapprehensions. To begin with, there are no bars, no nightclubs or public dance halls. Your home will be a palace in the wilder-ness, an ultra-modern monstrosity which will, neverthe-less, supply you with all the mod cons you are likely to need. The Neffetis, you understand, are following the behaviour pattern of the *nouveaux riches*. At present

they are like children let loose in a sweet shop, wanting
to try every flavour at one and the same time. To Euro-
peans it would appear only common sense to build such
palaces as are needed near to civilisation, but Arabs
pride themselves on a liking for the rigours of the desert
—they are, incidentally, a terribly snobbish race, very
conscious of their nobility—so they follow tradition and
build their new palaces in the isolation of the desert,
then pay fantastic sums to foreign interior decorators—
only the most famous will do—to cram the palaces with
the most awful collection of bric-à-brac they can find.

'However, I am relieved to be able to say that at last
some of the oil sheikhs are beginning to show qualities
of intelligence by turning their attention to the welfare
of the poor and needy of whom, even in Neffe, there are
still very many. The sheikhs have now acquired a thirst
for the benefits education bestows, and for their children they desire good manners and the air of refinement
you English insist upon imposing upon your children
from birth. Which is where you come in, Mademoiselle
Grey. Your job will be to turn two desert cubs, with
generations of nomadic freedom in their veins, into
models of propriety.'

His contemptuous tone aroused her indignation to
the extent of helping her to forget that there were other
more important matters on the agenda. 'Why don't you
employ a Frenchwoman to look after the children if you
despise the English so much?'

His lips went, if possible, a trifle thinner. 'On this
issue the Sheikh is adamant. Since the days of your first
Queen Elizabeth the British have wielded great influence over Neffetis who, in the manner of all impres-

sionable children, have been quick to imitate the less endearing traits of their so-called betters. Arabs, as I have already stated, are innately snobbish, and close proximity to the British has succeeded in turning what was a slight infection into an epidemic.'

Dove itched to slap her hand hard across the derogatory mouth, its sneer accentuated by the puckered scar. But too much was at stake, so she curbed the impulse and decided to ignore his taunts.

'You haven't given me time to explain,' she began. 'Mrs Todd told me——'

'To hold out for better terms?' he interrupted unpleasantly. 'Very well, you shall have more money. We usually pay a salary of four thousand pounds a year—if I increase it to five will that suffice?'

The offer rendered her speechless. Five thousand pounds for just one year's work! For that amount she would work for the devil! Oh, the joy of being able to tell her parents that all their problems were solved. Already she felt a blissful sense of relief; it was as if a great load had slid from her shoulders. And it was all due to this man!

When she searched for words to thank him his sardonic look reacted like the splash of cold water upon her hot cheeks. His contempt was so obvious she felt a quick spurt of tears, and recalled with shame the words he had hurled at Mrs Todd. '*Good riddance to your sex-starved, money-grabbing British nannies!*'

Then anger came to her aid. She had come prepared to be honest, to explain in detail why she so desperately needed the job, but his unjust prejudices made him unworthy of honesty. Besides that, it was doubtful whether he would believe a word she said ...

'Thank you, monsieur, you're very generous,' she told him crisply. 'Naturally I shall accept. But ...' her courage wilted, 'I must impose one condition.'

His brows beetled as he sent her a look of dark hauteur. 'It is lucky for you that you are in a seller's market, mademoiselle. What is this condition?'

Dove ran her tongue around lips that were suddenly dry. 'That ... I receive a year's salary in advance.'

Frigid silence fell. He brooded down at her from his great height, eyes narrowed to slits, arms folded across his chest in the manner of an imperious caliph about to pass judgment upon a disrespectful slave girl. She wanted to flee from the room, but her feet felt enmeshed in the deep pile carpet.

'Not one of your predecessors lasted more than a month,' he accused finally. 'What guarantee have I that you will remain longer?'

'My solemn promise ...?' she offered weakly.

'*Mon dieu!*' The depths of feeling displayed consigned her promise to Limbo.

Sensing her hopes fast disappearing, she pledged desperately, 'I'll put it in writing. Believe me, I'll sign anything, do anything ...!'

Immediately this confession was voiced she realised she had made a mistake in allowing him to see how badly she needed the job. A glint of satisfaction appeared in his eyes, a faint smile curled the twisted lip upwards.

'So, there is turbulence beneath the ice! Panic beneath the cool English exterior!' Once more, with irritating contempt, he snapped his fingers. 'Very well,' he decided, much to her surprise, 'if you promise to remain in my employment for not less than one year I shall write you out a cheque immediately for five thousand pounds—which sum shall entitle me to possess in its entirety one full year of your life!'

The ominously worded challenge was flung and courageously accepted. 'Very well, monsieur,' her eyes were grave, 'I agree.'

Without further hesitation he walked across to the writing desk, pulled his cheque book towards him, and swiftly began to write. The sound of tearing paper rasped across Dove's nerves, but she controlled her flinch and waited with composure as he advanced towards her carrying the cheque between thumb and forefinger.

'The price of your bondage, Mademoiselle Grey.' He proffered the cheque, with an expression of obvious distaste.

'Thank you.' Felling unbearably cheap, she stuffed it in her handbag and turned on her heel, anxious to put an end to the barter.

'*Un moment!*' The command was steel all through. 'I assume that your passport is up-to-date?' She nodded. 'Good, then here is an envelope containing details of necessary vaccinations and sundry other items of information you may find useful. Everything else can be left in my hands. I plan to leave for Neffe one week from today, can you be ready by then?'

'Certainly. All the clothes I'll need can be purchased in one day.'

'The Sheikh prefers nannies to dress in uniform.'

'Of course,' she flushed indignantly, 'I wouldn't

dream of doing otherwise when I'm on duty, but presumably I shall be allowed some time off?'

'Time in which to ensnare a rich husband, no doubt,' he drawled.

'Time in which to study an unfamiliar country,' she flashed. 'Time in which to recuperate from strenuous work—for make no mistake about it, monsieur, my job is not an easy one and I pride myself on being conscientious.'

'So conscientious you have not even bothered to ask one question about your charges,' he censured dryly. 'Can I be blamed for suspecting that they are of secondary importance?'

Dove gave an appalled start. She had indeed been remiss. Even though what she had endured had been not so much an interview as a battleground skirmish, it did not excuse such an oversight.

'Simply to satisfy any vague curiosity that may arise between now and our departure date,' he waxed sarcastic, 'I will tell you that you will have two children to look after, one of each sex. The elder, a girl, Bibi, is six years old and her brother, Salim, is almost three. The Sheikh's wife, Mariam, makes up his immediate family, but sundry cousins, nieces and nephews form his retinue. However, as your job will be to see to the children the rest of the household need not concern you.'

Feeling dismissed, she turned to go. 'Very well, monsieur. Goodbye, and thank you. I shall return here one week from today. Any particular time?'

'Seven in the morning,' he decided cruelly. 'When I have a long flight ahead of me I like to make an early start.'

If he had expected an adverse reaction he was disappointed. Children, perverse, demanding creatures that they were, had a penchant for wakening in the wee small hours with requests for food, drink, or simply attention. Dove had long since given up sleeping to a timetable.

She had almost reached the door when once again his voice reached her, grim and completely serious.

'Just one more request, mademoiselle!'

'Yes?' She turned a weary head, feeling incredibly buffeted, as spent as if she had just completed some severe manual task instead of a so-called civilised interview.

Cold grey eyes studied her across the width of the room. He must have been aware that what he was about to say was outrageous, but not so much as a shade of mockery crossed his aquiline features when he stipulated:

'I, too, must lay down a condition. You must *not*,' he stressed sternly, 'however much you are tempted, allow yourself to fall in love with me! Six times I have suffered cow-like looks from each of your predecessors, endured their unwanted company, their simpering attentions, until finally, after forcing me to be brutally frank, they collapsed into tears and begged to be allowed to return home. A seventh repeat of such a performance would be more than I could tolerate.'

Dove stared, appalled, eyes wide with disbelief, then finally managed to gasp, 'Believe me, monsieur, you need not worry on that account—you're in no danger from me!' Then, placing unflattering emphasis as she prepared to flee, *'Absolutely no danger at all!'*

Propelled by a sensation of dazed outrage, she found herself in the street. The man was mad, she decided, power-happy; his ruthless insensitivity might make him an ideal choice for the guardianship of a vulnerable family in a troubled land, but obviously the acquisition of so much authority had gone to his head.

The ordeal she had just suffered had left her in no mood for shopping, so she wandered the streets, marshalling her outraged thoughts, then made her way to the station from which her train was about to leave. She would just have time, she decided as she settled into a compartment, to reach the bank before closing time and deposit the precious cheque. This evening, when the day's work was over and she and her parents were relaxing after dinner, she would have the pleasure of flourishing her own personal cheque for four thousand pounds under her father's nose, seeing the strain disappear from his face and the happy light returning to her mother's eyes.

But the moment did not turn out quite as she had envisaged. They were sitting comfortably around the fire, her father with his long legs outstretched, looking unutterably weary, and her mother busily knitting, yet stopping so many times to count stitches it was clear she was finding it hard to concentrate. Relishing her big moment, the moment for which she had bartered a year of her life, Dove took the cheque from her pocket and as casually as she was able handed it to her father.

He grunted and heaved forward to scan the proffered piece of paper. At his gasp of surprise her mother's needles ceased clicking and she waited in a state of animated suspense for his comments.

'*How on earth...?*' He flashed Dove a look of astonishment. 'Where did you get all this money? You haven't been doing anything foolish, have you?'

When her mother saw for herself the amount written on the cheque she went so white Dove thought she was about to faint. 'Four thousand pounds! But how ...?' her bewildered eyes pleaded.

Sensing she would have to play it cool, Dove instilled mockery into her laughter. 'It's merely an advance on next year's salary, for heaven's sake! A concession from a grateful employer who's anxious to guarantee my services.'

'How very kind of him!' Her mother was pathetically easy to deceive.

Not so her father. Sharply he cross-examined, 'And who might your new employer be—the Aga Khan, perhaps?'

'You're almost there,' she twinkled, striving hard to keep the atmosphere light, determined at all costs to hide from her astute father the sensation of panic that soared through her at the mere mention of her new employer. 'Actually,' she told him airily, 'he's Sheikh Rahma bin Jabir who has employed me, by proxy, to look after his daughter Bibi and his son Salim.'

'A *sheikh*?' her mother almost shrieked.

'The Middle East ...!' Her father jumped to his feet. 'My dear child, don't you ever read the papers? Listen to news broadcasts ...? Every day there are reports of clashes between enemy factions, violent demonstrations and attempted assassinations.'

'Which are all highly exaggerated, I'm sure,' Dove hastened to assure him. 'As you've said yourself, many

times, one mustn't place too much reliance upon state-
ments made by the media, as they're often highly sen-
sationalised, small incidents blown up out of all propor-
tion in order to enliven an otherwise uneventful day.'

'You speak like a child,' her father rebuked sternly,
'with a child's ignorance of Middle Eastern affairs. In
one respect it might be true to say that some of the
matters reported are trivial, yet occurring as they do
within potentially explosive situations they're often the
spark that sets alight a dormant fuse. I'm sorry, Dove,'
he drew himself erect in a manner reminiscent of his
days of command, 'but I can't allow you to take on such
a hazardous job.' Firmly, the cheque was pushed into
her hand. 'Return this money immediately, together
with an apology to the Sheikh for any inconvenience
your impulsive decision might have caused him.'

'I was not interviewed by the Sheikh,' she protested,
'but even so, right this minute plans are being finalised,
I couldn't go back on my word.'

'You must!' She saw by the glint in her father's eyes
that a storm was brewing. 'If you don't feel you can
face the embarrassment of telling these people you've
changed your mind then I shall do it for you. Give me
an address where they can be reached.'

'No, Father!' Never in her life had Dove addressed
either of her parents with such adamancy. 'I've agreed
to take on the job—have even accepted an advance on
salary—so I shall carry on as promised. If my decision
upsets you then I'm sorry, because it was you who
taught me always to honour my promises.'

'But, Dove dear,' for the first time her mother interrupted in a tearful, quavering voice, 'you must try to

understand how we feel! You're our only child. Far rather we should face the consequences of bankruptcy than have the worry of knowing you to be in constant danger.'

Dove slipped an arm around her shoulders and gave her an affectionate hug. 'Put the thought of danger right out of your mind, Mother. I shall be perfectly safe with Monsieur Blais protecting the Sheikh's household.'

'Marc Blais?' Her father's head shot erect.

'Do you know him, Father?' Her expression reflected surprise.

'I know of him.' He resumed his seat, furrowed brow indicating a search into the recess of memory. 'To military men,' he told her slowly, 'the man's name is synonymous with courage and great bravery. When I first heard his name mentioned it was as an officer in the French Foreign Legion who, as a result of a hair-raising escapade in the desert during which he rescued a fellow officer from torture and almost certain death at the hands of renegade Arabs, was awarded the cross of the Légion d'Honneur. I can't recall the exact details, but the captured officer, as well as being a close friend of Marc Blais, was also supposed to be a son of some influential Arab family which, come to think of it, might explain his present day connection with Neffe.'

'The Foreign Legion,' Dove's nose wrinkled fastidiously, 'is made up of fugitives from justice, from their enemies, or simply from the responsibility of providing for a wife and children, isn't it?'

Her father laughed, seeming, for some reason, much less worried than he had been a few minutes previously.

'Your image of the Foreign Legion has obviously been gleaned from romantic fiction,' he teased. 'The fact is, the Legion is no longer a collection of misfits and love-lorn adventurers, but is most selective, choosing its recruits from the cream of today's youth who, after ruthless discipline and stringent training, emerge as Legionnaires capable of enduring the worst physical conditions in desert or jungle and who are noted for their insistence upon fighting to the very last man. I must admit, Dove, to feeling fewer qualms now that I know you are to be in charge of a member of one of the Régiments Etrangers, for the corollary of a Legionnaire is his willingness to battle against all odds and to use any means to improve those odds, neither giving nor ex-pecting any quarter.'

In spite of the warmth of the room she shivered. In-stead of being reassuring, as no doubt he had intended, her father had increased her fears about the barbaric man who was to be her immediate boss. In spite of her father's glowing testimonial, she felt the Legion was suspect, with a reputation for cruelty which must have been superimposed upon every member of its ranks. It could be argued that the French Government, being ashamed of its Legion's reputation, had decided to apply a coat of whitewash in the form of favourable publicity and had succeeded so well in that even men as knowledgeable as her father had been deceived. Having just recently clashed with one of the legendary Legion-naires, however, she felt more inclined towards her original belief, which was that the Legion recruited its men from the slums, the refugee camps, and the prisons of the world. Men who fought, not for France because they owed her no allegiance, but for more sinister reasons. They were mercenaries, men who were prepared to kill for money. If such men were as merciless and hard-bitten as they were reputed to be then it followed that their commanding officers must be a hundred times more so!

From the depths of memory emerged a few sentences contained within the only book she had ever read concerning the Legion. The author, a deserter, had been bitter in his indictment.

'Only ignorant fools and glamour-struck boys join the Legion. If conditions inside the ranks were made public the force would become extinct because of lack of volunteers. Simply donning the uniform bestows arrogance—*men become beasts before wearing it for a year!*'

# CHAPTER FOUR

THE discovery that they were to fly to Neffe by private jet surprised Dove. On a grey cheerless morning, in a mood reflective of the atmosphere, Monsieur Blais ushered her aboard the silver plane, then, showing as little concern for her as he did towards the stowing of the remaining baggage, helped her aboard, then strapped himself into a seat on the opposite side of the aisle before proceeding to concentrate his attention upon papers protruding from a still-bulging briefcase.

When the engines roared into life every nerve of her body tensed. With clenched fists and the dry taste of fear in her mouth she watched houses, fields and hedges whizzing past, then closed her eyes as the plane gathered speed, ready for lift-off. Feeling certain a crash was imminent, yet determined not to communicate to the unfeeling brute opposite that this was her very first flight, she withdrew into a tense knot of silence.

After an agony of time she forced open her eyes and saw below a sea of cottonwool cloud with above it a sky of brilliant blue whose existence, as she had crossed the windswept runway, she had never suspected.

'That pea-green complexion suits you,' a callous voice mocked. 'In a pocket at the side of your seat you will find plastic bags—please use one if you are going to be sick.'

'I've no intention of being sick, thank you all the same,' Dove gritted.

When he shrugged his indifference and returned to his papers she relaxed, anxious to enjoy this new experience. Life from now on was to be full of adventure instead of humdrum routine; she must learn to adapt, physically and mentally, to whatever demands might be made upon her.

Only once during the five-hour flight did she look his way, and only then because, sensing a hard stare, some inner mechanism goaded her to retaliate. But when she had turned her head he had been engrossed in his papers, so she had shrugged, blaming her own overactive imagination, and tried to force an interest in the magazine which for the past half hour had lain unopened on her lap. But her mind was so troubled she could not concentrate. Conscience kept insisting that she was here under false pretences. If only she had been honest with him, contradicted his assumption that she had been sent by Mrs Todd, she would not now be fretting about the consequences should he ever discover he had been tricked.

A young Arab steward served breakfast, accompanied by incomparably delicious coffee served in tiny cups. Having eaten nothing since supper the previous evening she was able to do justice to bitter-sweet grapefruit, oven-crisp rolls with creamy butter, and a generous platter of bacon, egg and sausages. When Monsieur Blais waved away all but the coffee she felt ashamed of her greed.

'That is probably exactly how he intends me to feel!' she muttered to herself, angrily spearing a sausage. 'It wouldn't surprise me to discover that, like the camel, he's trained himself to go without sustenance for weeks!'

In an effort to ignore his disturbing presence, she finished her coffee, then settled her head on the back of her seat, closed her eyes, and willed herself to sleep. The past week had been sheer turmoil—shopping, paying last-minute visits to relatives and friends, writing letters and making all the arrangements necessary for her year of exile. Consequently she had slept very little, so was able after a while to slide into a doze that lasted more than an hour, during which time they flew out of cloud into sunshine so brilliant that when she eventually awoke she had difficulty in focusing upon the first thing she saw, a wing of the aircraft—a sword of molten silver stabbing so brilliantly it was hurtful to the eyes.

'You sleep, mademoiselle, as one with an untroubled mind.'

Immediately on the defensive, she jerked, 'Is there any reason why I shouldn't?' Blood pounded through her veins as she waited for his answer. If he harboured any suspicions at all now was his chance to take up her challenge!

'English females share one similarity with their Eastern sisters,' he drawled. 'Both shelter behind a veil of innocence. However, it is not unknown for a woman of the harem to suffer a thrashing for her misdeeds.'

'A thrashing? From whom ...?' Dove gasped.

'From their lord and master, who else?' His eyebrows arched, indicating genuine surprise.

'Then it's just as well,' she reminded him with asperity, 'that I don't possess one.'

'Oh, but you do.' His answer was traced with silken threat. 'Have you not sold yourself into bondage for one year? And did I not pay the very high price you consider you are worth? To all intents and purposes, mademoiselle, I am your master.'

'Don't be ridiculous!' she gasped. 'How can you speak of bondage in this day and age?'

For the first time in their acquaintance he smiled, a brief lifting of the lips that projected derision rather than amusement. Pushing aside his briefcase, he leant sideways to emphasise, 'With each step taken into the desert a century of civilisation is left behind. In the cities and suburbs there are signs of degeneration—Arab women dressed by Dior preening at endless coffee mornings and cocktail parties, playing golf, learning to ride, in fact, aping their Western sisters in any way they can. Yet for the most part they are pathetic beings, soaked in luxury and loneliness, knowing that in spite of their pitiful attempts to appear liberated their husbands' religion forbids that they should ever be regarded as equals. The lowly status of womankind is an incontrovertible fact among men of the East. For did not the blessed prophet say: "I stood at the gate of paradise and lo! most of its inhabitants were the poor. And I stood at the gate of hell and lo! most of its inhabitants were women! Moreover, Arab men firmly believe that woman was made out of a crooked rib of Adam which if you tried to bend it would break and if you left it alone would always remain crooked.

'So you see, mademoiselle, you must put away for a year all your misconceptions about women being equal, for once you enter an Arab's household you will become part of a lower creation, on the same plane as his wife, who very often may not even eat her meals with her lord who devours his food apart from her and allows her to eat only when he has finished—unless, of course, he desires her to administer to his amusement and pleasure.'

It would have been very easy to scream at him to turn the plane around so that she might return home, but bravely she swallowed back panic that had risen in a lump to her throat and decided that he was trying to frighten her. He must not be allowed to guess that he had succeeded. There was cruelty in the cold grey eyes searching her face for signs of reaction. It was not difficult to image him exerting his authority over a squad of Legionnaires, marching them miles through the heat of the desert, supporting huge knapsacks, rifles, bayonets, shovels, ammunition and wood for fires—all this in full uniform, including an army greatcoat. Ordering his sergeants to chivvy along any stragglers and, when a man became too exhausted to obey, having him dragged behind the mule cart that brought up the rear of every column. No doubt he would try to justify such cruelty by quoting the Legion's slogan: March or Die, and pointing out that a man could not hope to survive unless he kept his place in the column, but as she stared into the bleak eyes, the hawk-like features that were never softened by a smile, she knew that this desert Legionnaire was devoid of compassion and that far from regretting the need to impose discipline he would revel in the duty.

The plane landed on a private airstrip stuck, or so it seemed to her, in the midst of desert wasteland, a mysterious primitive landscape composed of sand, gravel and an oppressively blank sky that stretched, miles and miles of it, from horizon to flat horizon. As Dove stepped from the air-conditioned plane she gasped. It was afternoon, the sun was at its hottest, so that when she met its fierce heat it was as if she had stepped out of a cool shower into the heat of a fire.

Within the short time it took to walk across to a waiting Landrover her nylon blouse was attached to her body like a second skin and the medium-weight suit she had considered just right for the transition from cold climate to hot assumed the oppressive burden of a fur coat in a heatwave.

Monsieur Blais had discarded the overcoat he had worn while boarding the plane and, looking coolly acclimatised in a light grey suit and pristine shirt dramatically offset by a flow of maroon tie, took the seat next to her in the Landrover, then crisply ordered the driver to move on.

To where? So far as Dove could see there was absolutely no sign of habitation filtering through the heat haze. The car was travelling on a road of sorts, hard-packed sand imprinted with tyre marks from cars and lorries, but seemingly without end, just a wriggling snake dropping over the edge of the far horizon.

'Why didn't the Sheikh build his airstrip closer to the palace?' she ventured.

The forbidding profile did not turn. He seemed preoccupied, his eyes scanning the panorama of nothingness as if he could see many things that she could not. Yet he deigned, with a pained tolerance that made her feel about eight years old, to explain. 'We thought it more convenient for everyone concerned to site it halfway between the palace and the community housing the men brought out here to develop and maintain the oil fields.' He glanced sideways and the sight of her wilting figure seemed to exacerbate his notorious impatience. '*Ciel*! Don't tell me you are preparing to complain already! You English are such moaners, always when you travel you expect the best of everything—the best accommodation, the best food, the best transport available! Do you consider your race has a divine right to the best and, if so, what, as a nation, have you ever done to merit such conceit?'

The contempt in which he held the English was galling. At any other time she might have been tempted into argument, but discretion warned her to hold her tongue. There was no way a fierce desert hawk was going to be outwitted by a broiled chicken!

The relief when the outline of a building hove into view was indescribable. At first it appeared so vague it might have been a mirage, but as they advanced towards it she made out the shapes of domes, towers, arches, and ornamented corbels supporting upper windows. A tall, solid wall surrounded the whole.

They drove through wrought iron gates, opened in readiness by a sharp-eyed concierge, and proceeded along a drive bordered by a profusion of flowering shrubs, tamarisks, and palms. Neat paths branched off into gardens and as they neared the front of the house she caught a glimpse of lawns, fountains, and the deep blue depths of a mosaic-lined swimming pool. She resisted an impulse to rub her eyes. The sudden plunge from blasting heat into the cool green oasis was confusing. Obviously the Sheikh was a man who liked his comfort and possessed money enough to satisfy his every whim. It would not surprise her in the least to discover a miniature Everest somewhere within the domain, complete with snow slopes, ski-lift, the lot!

When the car halted at the foot of a flight of stone steps Monsieur Blais ushered her indoors. Seeming to read her thoughts, he confirmed grimly, 'The Sheikh is a prodigious spender. In all, he has seven palaces, but this one is his favourite. The entire place has been reconditioned regardless of expense and is now one of the most magnificent residences in the whole of Neffe. Reception and banqueting rooms can accommodate three hundred guests at one sitting; each of the many bedrooms is fitted out with ultra-modern conveniences and the whole place is equipped with close-circuit television. He has even had a golf course laid out—not for himself, because he does not play—simply for the benefit of any guests that might.'

A golf course in the flaming desert!

The fairy-tale palace with hand-carved ceilings painted blue, crimson and gold had an entrance hall of pink marble, the fountain in its centre filled with flowers instead of water jets, and a pair of crimson-carpeted stairways ascending steeply into the upper quarters. Inlaid ivory and ebony tables were ranged against panelled walls, small arched niches housed a jumble of costly vases and ornaments. At the far end of the room was a raised dais covered with rugs and a low divan piled with cushions arranged along three sides. Set in the wall behind the divan was a large window composed of small pieces of coloured glass let into a framework of stucco, so as to form a floral pattern that admitted colourful half-light, a jewelled cascade spilling splashes of blue, green, mauve and gold upon the marbled floor.

Hurrying in the wake of the stalking Frenchman, Dove tried to catch up and almost cannoned into him when he halted suddenly and spun on his heel. A shaft of coloured sunlight became trapped in her hair, its rosy glow bestowing upon her fair head the tint of pink champagne.

At that moment, unnoticed by either of them, a heavy velvet door curtain was swished aside and a man stepped into the room. He halted, his eyes fixed upon Dove who, blithely unconscious of his hard scrutiny, was staring blissfully around wearing an expression of bemused delight.

'Flower of the desert,' he breathed his admiration. 'Wine is thy body, music thy countenance, and untold joy is their offspring!'

Dove heard nothing, but saw Monsieur Blais's eyes narrow to slits and his scar standing out white against an outthrust jaw. Her eyes sought the object of his displeasure and recoiled from the intimacy of a hot, roving glance.

'Greetings, Marc!' Almost immediately the man's expression changed to one of suave urbanity.

'And to you, Zaid.' Gravely Marc Blais inclined his head.

The antagonism between the two men was almost tangible. Dove shivered, disliking on sight this new generation of Arab whose fleshy features spoke of over-indulgence, whose hands looked plump and soft, whose eyes transmitted messages that filled her with revulsion.

With his eyes fastened upon her face he waited for the introduction Marc Blais seemed reluctant to offer.

'And you are ...?' He extended his hand in a show of Western manners and, inwardly cringing, Dove brushed her finger-tips against his.

'Miss Grey, who has done us the honour of accepting the post of children's nanny.' Dove could hardly believe the evidence of her own ears. 'Miss Grey,' Monsieur Blais continued, 'may I introduce Zaid, younger brother of Sheikh Rahma.'

'An Englishwoman...?' When she nodded he smiled. 'I admire your taste, Marc.' Then addressing Dove, he pleaded, 'Do not, Miss Grey, allow him to chase you away as he has chased away your predecessors whose unveiled beauty and tantalising petticoats enlivened our lives for far too short an interval.'

Mercifully she was saved the effort of a reply when Marc Blais cut in sharply, 'Where is Sheikh Rahma? We have a great deal of business to discuss; as he knew my time of arrival I half expected him to be waiting for me.'

Zaid shrugged. 'You know as well as I do that my brother's inclinations run closer to pleasure than to business. He is at present occupied with his latest plaything—a highly bred stallion sent to him as a gift by the ruler of a neighbouring state but one, who will be expecting, and will no doubt receive, a brace of Cadillacs in return. But tell me,' his tone quickened, 'how did the armaments deal go? Have you managed to secure the promise of all we need?'

'The results of my business transactions are no affair of yours. Later, if your brother sees fit, you may be taken into his confidence, but from me you will learn nothing.'

Unadulterated fury blazed in Zaid's eyes as he tried to weather the tersely worded insult. Dove stared, fascinated and a little afraid, at the man trying so hard to control his anger. If Monsieur Blais was a desert hawk then this man was a fox, cunning, treacherous, sly and with, she guessed, a passion for revenge that would outlast time itself.

Instinctively she chose the protection of the hawk by moving closer to his side.

In a voice shaking with feeling Zaid threatened, 'At this moment, Frenchman, my brother is in control. But sheikhdoms have been known to topple, and if this one ever does then the debt my brother owes you could quite easily be overlooked by those who take over command.'

'I wouldn't have it any other way,' the Frenchman assured him smoothly, 'for if that day ever dawns I shall know I have failed in my duty to the man whose family I am pledged to protect. But believe me, Zaid, it is not your destiny to rule,' his look of searing contempt traced the Arab from head to toe. 'You are soft and flabby both in body and mind—no true Arab would pledge his allegiance to a man of straw!'

When the enraged Zaid had swept speechless from the room Dove felt impelled to register a protest. 'Did you have to show your antagonism quite so plainly? Weakling or not, I suspect that that man would make a dangerous enemy, so couldn't you have at least pretended——'

'No, mademoiselle, I could not! It is not in my nature to pretend. To me, friendship implies trust—I would never pitch my tent where I dared not rest my head.'

The sound of clattering hooves outside the palace, of many voices loud with jest and pleasurable laughter, brought their conversation to an abrupt end.

'There's Rahma now!' Marc Blais began striding towards the door. 'Stay here while I greet him, I'll return as soon as I can.'

'Well!' Feeling like a discarded mongrel, Dove slumped down on to a stool and prepared to wait. 'Your wish is my command, oh, master!' she snapped in the direction of his retreating back. 'May Allah take pity on my parched tongue, for obviously you will not!'

But less than ten minutes had elapsed when he returned accompanied by an Arab who she immediately guessed was the Sheikh. The two men strode the length of the room deep in conversation. Even from a distance a bond of friendship was evident, the Sheikh's arm resting upon the Frenchman's shoulders as they walked, his face, gravely intent, yet with eyes that rested upon his friend holding the affection of a brother. He was tall, standing eye to eye with the other man, and his body was equally slim. Piercing brown eyes, firm, sculptured lips, and thick, bushy eyebrows combined to produce a handsome if intimidating face. He was wearing a light cloak threaded with gold over a white tunic beaded around the edges, and a red chequered head-cloth kept in place with thick black double cord. Riding boots polished until the leather appeared blood red, and a necklace of jewelled charms, completed the picture. As he spoke he waved his hand so that sunlight glistened upon a gold ring, a long, brown, shapely hand typical of the Arab *élite*.

When they strode past her without a glance indignation drove her to her feet.

'Excuse me...!' she began, then faltered into silence when the Sheikh's haughty stare swivelled in her direction. Too late, she remembered being told that in the Arab world one did not address high personages until invited to do so. She blushed, intimidated by beetling brows, and felt enormously grateful when Marc Blais came to her rescue.

'*Mon dieu*, I had forgotten about you!' At any other time she would have felt furious. 'Rahma, this young lady is Miss Grey, the children's new nanny.'

When the Sheikh acknowledged her presence with a courteous nod she was almost tempted to curtsey. Then he frowned, directing at Monsieur Blais a look of censure. 'Miss Grey looks exhausted. When will you remember, my friend, that not every European adjusts as well as yourself to our climate?' He laughed, turning back to Dove. 'Though I must confess that he has been so long in our country we Arabs regard him as one of us. Would you believe, Miss Grey, that although every luxury is placed at his disposal, this desert nomad prefers to sleep on the floor of his room with a pillow of sand beneath his head?'

She could quite easily believe it, but aware that

criticism from her direction would not be tolerated by the man smiling fondly at his friend she merely smiled, pretending amusement.

The Sheikh clapped his hands and from out of nowhere appeared a servant. 'Coffee and sweetmeats,' he demanded. Then with a wave of his hand he directed Dove towards the divan. 'Might I suggest, Miss Grey, that after you have taken refreshments you retire to the rooms that have been prepared for you? You must do nothing for the rest of today. Naturally, the children are eagerly awaiting your arrival, but they must contain their curiosity until morning.'

As she was thanking him, the Sheikh's personal coffee server stalked into the room, a dignified, impressive old man wearing a long black robe, carrying in one hand a large brass coffee pot with a curved spout and in the other a nest of tiny handleless cups. Slowly he poured a meagre amount of the fragrant liquid into each cup, then served first his master, then Marc Blais, and finally Dove herself.

Sitting with her legs folded awkwardly beneath her on the low divan, she envied the effortless ease with which the men were able to relax.

'There are rules to this coffee game.' Marc Blais helped her to a paper-thin pastry layered with almonds and honey. 'To take three cups of coffee is traditionally correct, but if you want more there is no need to hold out your cup. When you have had sufficient you simply hand back your cup with a small shake of dismissal— otherwise it will be refilled until eternity.'

'Filled ...?' Her look disparaged the small amount of coffee contained within her cup.

'To an Arab a filled cup is an implied insult—Drink up and go as soon as you can!'

'Which sentiment certainly does not apply to you, Miss Grey,' the Sheikh assured her graciously. '*Ahlan wa sahlan!*—You are indeed welcome!' As if recalling her many predecessors, he enquired testily, 'I hope, Marc, that you have impressed upon Miss Grey how imperative it is that she does stay for at least a year? The children are becoming unsettled by constant change.'

'She will stay.' Laconically, Marc Blais eyed her. 'Miss Grey owes it to me, and whatever their faults the English do not shirk from paying their debts.'

- *A Rose For Danger*
  **-Marquerite Bell**
- *Francesca*
  **-Valentina Luellen**
- *Madelon*
  **-Valentina Luellen**

# CHAPTER FIVE

ALMOST everything in the nursery was blue, including carpets, miniature items of furniture, and curtains that billowed in the breeze from an open window guarded by safety bars. A collection of costly presents, silver eggcups, spoons, rattles, ivory teething rings, were displayed on shelves ranged around the walls.

As Dove stepped inside, looking crisply efficient in a uniform dress of pale grey, collared and cuffed in white organdie, the occupants looked up. The children, she noted with relief, were both dressed in Western clothes. The girl, Bibi, brown-eyed, dark-haired and with down-turned lips betraying a hint of petulance, wore a pink cotton sundress and Salim, a mere toddler, was in a trouser suit of the inevitable blue.

A young nurserymaid scrambled to her feet when Dove approached, discarding the clockwork toy she had been winding for Salim. Indignantly, he emitted a wail of protest which, when it was ignored, escalated into a shriek of fury so penetrating it actually hurt the ears. This seemingly much-used ploy had the desired effect upon the nurserymaid, who immediately dropped to her knees to attend to his needs. Dove's heart sank. The boy was obviously spoiled, demanding and receiving attention at his slightest murmur. Even his sister, for all her tender years, seemed resigned to existing in the shadow of the rampant young male.

She steeled herself to be cruel. Salim was an engaging child, a merry-eyed, curly-haired individualist, but already, she guessed, an adept at probing the limits of adult tolerance. Unfortunately, such behaviour was not confined to the nurseries of the East; she had met it before. So, following guidelines laid down during her training, she decided upon tactics which hitherto had gained dramatic results.

Briskly, pretending the child did not exist, she stepped past him and approached his sister. Gently smiling, she extended a hand. 'Good morning, you must be Bibi.' The girl nodded shy confirmation. 'I am your new nanny, Miss Grey. Tell me, Bibi, have you had breakfast yet?'

'No, Miss Grey. Alya said we must wait for you.'

'Alya being the nurserymaid?' Dove swung round to smile at the young girl who seemed undecided whether to rise to her feet or to remain crouched at Salim's side. 'I'm sorry, Alya, that I didn't put in an appearance earlier. I could have done, because I awoke early, but I didn't expect to find the children up so soon.'

'Everyone here rises early, Miss Grey,' the girl explained shyly, 'so as to get done as much as possible before the sun is at its hottest. The children then sleep for an hour or two after their midday meal.'

'Thank you for putting me right, Alya. I shall have to rely upon you a lot in the future—to tell me what the children like to eat, for instance, and where they are allowed to play. Some part of their day must be spent outside of the nursery, delightful though it is. Whoever planned the décor had a decided preference for blue.'

Casually she tossed the conversational ball, hoping Alya would respond. Out of the corner of her eye she could see Salim's outraged face, his pouting lip pronounced as he struggled with the unfamiliar sensation of being ignored.

'Blue is a lucky colour.' Alya deserted her charge. 'It is said to ward off the evil eye. All Arab children wear blue beads, the girls as earrings or bracelets and the boys have them sewn on to their caps. Even donkeys and camels can be seen with them strung around their necks, and if ever you are in an Arab village you will see that all the door-frames are painted blue.'

'How interesting!' Dove stooped to examine Bibi. 'Then where are your lucky blue beads? I cannot see a necklace, a brooch, or earrings ...?'

Triumphantly the child held out a foot encased in an embroidered slipper. 'Today, I am wearing them on my shoes!'

This deep interest in a mere girl was more than Salim could stand. Quickly he scrambled to his feet and toddled across the room until he could reach out to tug the hem of Dove's skirt.

'Beads...!' He waved a plumb brown wrist encircled by a bracelet of brilliant blue. 'Salim, beads...!'

'Yes, darling, I see,' Dove smiled, resisting an impulse to gather the engaging little bundle into her arms. Keeping her voice casual, she suggested, 'Now that we're all acquainted, I think we should eat, don't you?'

Breakfast could have been a hilarious affair had she not applied her own brand of quiet discipline, so that the interlude passed without a repeat of Salim's earlier behaviour even though once, after she had rebuked him for pouring milk upon the floor, the threat of a tantrum trembled in the air. This was averted by the simple expedient of distracting his attention, and as the morning progressed and peace continued to reign, Alya voiced her amazement.

'You have cast a magic spell, Miss Grey. Usually at this time of the day the nursery is bedlam. Salim is always cross first thing in the morning, and Bibi does not help by teasing him into a frenzy.'

'But what did the previous nannies do? Couldn't they restore order?'

Alya shrugged. 'They tried, for the first few days at least, but then they seemed to give up and allowed the children to have their own way. Because of this, the nursery has become taboo to visitors around this hour —even the children's mother can't stand the noise.'

'I was just about to ask you about her.' Absently, Dove guided Salim's hand, holding a paintbrush, towards a pot of paint and nodded approval when he managed to transfer a thick splosh of yellow on to a page of his drawing book. 'Presumably she spends part of the day with the children. Does she come here to the nursery or do they have to be taken to her rooms?'

'They don't see her *every* day, she just pops into the nursery whenever the fancy takes her.'

Which probably was not very often, Dove guessed from what the girl had not said. To be a mother, in her opinion, was one of the greatest privileges bestowed upon woman, yet as she had experienced so often in the past, to some women it was a privilege that was highly overrated. Philosophically, she shrugged. Were it not for such women hundreds of nannies, herself included, would be unemployed.

When later that morning she was summoned into the presence of Mariam, the children's mother, she had a half-formed impression of that lady in her mind, but the reality, as she was shown into a sumptuous apartment dimmed by closely-drawn shutters, transported her straight into the mystique of the Arabian Nights. Draped across a silken couch was a girl of enchanting loveliness, slender and graceful as the twig of an oriental willow. Dusky locks fell in a cascade to her waist and a mole like a drop of ambergris drew notice to a full, ruby-red mouth. Almond-shaped eyes, intensely black and brilliant, were softened by long silken lashes outlined by a border of kohl. Her eyebrows were thin and arched, her forehead wide, and small, tapering fingers were dyed with the deep orange red of henna. With languid interest she watched Dove approaching, then waved her towards a cushioned stool before deliberating, fingers greedily poised, over a huge box of chocolates.

'Sit down, Miss Grey.' Her voice was husky and unhurried. 'Tell me, now that you have had time to make their acquaintance, what do you think of my children?'

Regaining her composure, Dove took the seat indicated and spoke the truth. 'They are both delightful, if a little spoiled.'

A complacent smile curled Mariam's lips as she bit deeply into a chocolate. 'We Arabs indulge our children, it does them no harm.'

Dove swallowed hard. 'There I must disagree. Children need discipline as much as they need food—indeed, without discipline their maturity is very much impeded.'

Almond-shaped eyes betrayed a flash of hauteur. 'Are you implying, Miss Grey, that my children are backward?'

'Indeed not,' Dove smiled. 'They are both intelligent and gifted children who, unfortunately, have been allowed to make up their own rules as they go along. This will have to stop,' she spoke firmly but without heat. 'If they are to grow up into stable young adults they must be made aware of the needs for rules within a mature, independent society.'

'Pooh!' With a wave of her hand Mariam dismissed this point of view, then prepared once again to tackle the weighty problem of choosing another chocolate. 'Salim will grow up to make rules, not to obey them! As for Bibi,' she shrugged, 'the laws of the harem are simple and few.'

'But,' Dove leant forward in eagerness, 'can a man be expected to give orders if he has never learnt to obey them? And what if Bibi should decide against life in a harem? Arab girls are becoming liberated: schools, hospitals, even colleges are being built by progressive-minded sheikhs who want the very best for their children. By the time Bibi has grown up it may be commonplace for girls such as she to become teachers, doctors, scientists, as they already do in most Western countries.'

Mariam lost interest in the chocolates and regarded Dove with eyes holding a glimmer of interest.

'Marc was right—you are very forthright! Tell me more about the women of the West. I'm not sure I would like to live as they do, but until I know more about them I cannot compare their lives with my own.'

'Well,' Dove hesitated, 'there are so many differences I hardly know where to begin. To start with, Western society has decreed that women must be placed on an equal footing with men—equal opportunities, equal rights in the eyes of the law, and equal pay for those doing the same jobs as men.'

Mariam shuddered delicately. 'I should not care to do men's work.' She preened, running a hand down the length of her slender body. 'Practising the art of seduction is time-consuming enough, if it is done well. Some days I am exhausted by the effort of preparing my body for my husband's pleasure. How do Western women find the time to do this and cope with a career?'

Wryly, Dove smiled, glimpsing for the first time the enormity of the gap between her own sort and beauties of the harem. 'They don't, I'm afraid. They rather expect men to concentrate upon pleasing *them*.'

Mariam stared, scandalised. 'If I were to act in such a manner, Rahma would cast me aside in favour of one of his other wives!'

'One—one of his *other*? How many wives does he have?'

'Four,' Mariam beamed proudly. 'But I am his favourite because I'm the only one who has given him a son. Soon, Rahma intends me to be once again with child, and if it should turn out to be another boy then my position in his household will become strengthened.'

'And what if it's a girl?'

Mariam pouted. 'I shall still be secure, but he will

probably divorce one of his older wives and take to himself a younger bride.' There was no rancour in her voice, just the fatalism of the East, an inbred acceptance that what will be will be, and a lack of enthusiasm for change which was probably the reason why the role of desert men had remained the same since Adam.

'Don't you ever feel frustrated?' Dove tried not to sound as exasperated as she felt. 'How do you pass the time?'

Mariam seemed surprised that she should need to ask. 'I sit on this sofa—and when I am tired I cross over to sit on that one! Sometimes Rahma takes me to call upon friends and there I hear the latest gossip, eat sweetmeats, discuss clothes, and am entertained by singers and dancers. I lead a very busy life!'

Dove could find no words to combat such complacency. Completely devoid of education, Mariam could not begin to understand higher or more intellectual pleasures than those her physical senses could appreciate. To eat, to dress, to chatter, to sleep, to dream away the sultry hours on a divan, to stimulate her husband's affections—*And she actually called that living!*

She was glad to return to the comparative sanity of the nursery. As she closed the door of Mariam's apartment behind her and began walking along the passageway her steps quickened as the sound of yelling and screaming penetrated the nursery door. She was only halfway there when a tall figure appeared, striding from the opposite end of the passageway. When they met outside the door she recognised saturnine features clamped with irritation.

'You are conforming to type, Miss Grey. In common with others of your kind you allow personal pursuits to take precedence over your duties. If you can spare the time,' he continued, heavily sarcastic, 'would you please put a stop to that boy's infernal screeching?'

'I have not been——' she began stormily.

'Spare me the excuses, I've heard them all before. All I want is to be allowed to concentrate upon the mountain of paperwork that has accumulated during my absence. This is not possible while the child continues to exercise his lungs. Well, what are you waiting for?' he barked when indignation kept her frozen to the spot. 'Are you going to put a stop to it or shall I?'

When a particularly raucous scream assaulted their ears he muttered savagely beneath his breath and, giving her no time to react, flung open the nursery door.

Bedlam, she thought, leaning weakly against the doorjamb, would be considered a rest camp compared with this! The room was in an uproar, blobs of various-coloured paint were splattered all over the walls and the dish of water the children had been using to clean their brushes had been dashed to the floor, spilling its streaky contents over a priceless blue and cream rug. Alya was cowering in a corner, completely at a loss how to deal with the pair of young savages rolling on the floor locked in combat. Splashes of vivid paint outstanding on Bibi's hair indicated a possible reason for the fracas, but Salim, whose arrogance was incredible in one so young, was obviously taking exception to being chastised for his misdeed.

'*Mon dieu!*' The blasphemy barely had time to register before Marc Blais swooped, grabbed each of them by the scruff of the neck, and tore them apart. 'How dare you indulge in such disgraceful behaviour!' He shook them until their teeth rattled, then set them upon their feet a yard apart. Stepping back, he fixed them with a cold, vexed stare, daring them to move. Transfixed, they did not flex a muscle while, without turning his head, he addressed Dove.

'As from this moment, I wish to see more discipline exerted over the inhabitants of this nursery. These two have been indulged almost beyond repair—you do realise, mademoiselle,' the irony of his voice was very obvious, 'that part of your job is to help mould the characters of the children in your care? This boy,' Salim, the infant, quivered beneath his scrutiny, 'will one day be ruler of this sheikhdom. How can he be expected to master an army if he has not been taught to master his own temper? And as for you, Bibi!' his voice did not soften as he scolded the girl, 'your behaviour was hardly what one might expect of your mother's daughter.'

When tears sprang to Bibi's eyes Dove broke the rule of a lifetime and darted forward to range with the children against their chastiser. 'You expect too much, monsieur! They're only infants, both of them, yet you speak as if to sages. Youth and wisdom make odd wheels for a cart!'

An astounded hush fell, broken after endless seconds by a snigger that came from the direction of the corner where Alya still cowered, a fascinated spectator. Marc Blais's lips thinned. With her eyes raised no higher than the angry scar pulsating against an outthrust jaw, Dove heard his command.

'First of all, mademoiselle, you will supervise the clearing up of the nursery. One hour should be sufficient. When that hour has passed I shall expect to see you downstairs in my office.'

The children's sympathy, as soberly and methodically they helped to erase the results of their naughtiness, should have been comforting but, oddly, it was not. It was as if they were mutely transmitting condolences, their half-fearful, half-admiring glances most unnerving, Alya did not help when, on a note of breathless awe, she confided:

'You are very brave, Miss Grey.' She shivered, as if the consequences of such bravery were more than she dared contemplate.

'Nonsense!' Dove replied briskly, subduing a sudden surge of dread. 'I'm sure Monsieur Blais's bark is far worse than his bite.'

To her annoyance, Alya shook her head. 'That is not so, Miss Grey. Men say of him that he can endure the unendurable, many times his strength has been tested by adversity, as gold is tested by fire. But it is also said of him that his heart is as cold as that of the basilisk who, with one look, can turn creatures into stone. Many women have attempted to disprove this, but have succeeded only in arousing his devilish wrath. Do you suppose that is his attraction?' she whispered, running the tip of her tongue around lips parted with awe, *'the fatal fascination of a sinner!'*

In spite of herself, Dove shivered. The man had the arrogance of the devil, no doubt of that, and his dark, razor-edged features, derisive mouth, the scar that hinted at violent passion lying dormant beneath an

ice-cold surface, combined to form a satanic attraction
some women might find irresistible. *Don't fall in love
with me*, he had demanded, the weary resignation
threading through the command proof that many
women already had.

How could they possibly? questioned her stunned
mind. Love, in her limited experience, was epitomised
by the devotion, tenderness and respect shown to each
other by her parents. Monsieur Blais frightened the
life out of her!

'Don't be childish, Alya!' The fear in her voice
sounded to the maid like irritation. 'And don't ever
again make such observations in this nursery.'

With inexorable stealth, the hands of her watch crept
round to the fateful hour. The nursery was once again
spick and span, the children settled down for their
afternoon nap, when with pounding nerves and slightly
sticky palms, Dove hesitated outside the door of Marc
Blais's office, willing up the courage to knock. When
finally she did so his terse : *'Entrez!'* sent her stumbling
inside where, seated in a leather chair placed behind a
huge, workmanlike desk, with shelves of books ranged
around him, he looked master of all he surveyed.

'Take a seat.' Frostily he indicated a chair placed
directly in front of him, then continued for long humiliating minutes writing swiftly in a black, sloping hand.

Dove waited with eyes cast down, hands clasped
loosely in her lap, erasing all traces of the resentment
she felt from her expressive face. He had obviously
decided she should be humbled and this was his way of
showing how little she mattered, how unimportant
were her bruised feelings.

As his pen continued racing across the page, her mind wandered back to other positions she had held, recalling small courtesies extended by members of households eager to make her feel at home. Men had always risen to their feet whenever she had entered a room, had enquired if everything in the nursery was satisfactory, had often insisted upon her sharing a glass of sherry with the family before dinner, and many—if she had not firmly declined—would have been pleased to have her join them for their evening meal.

Here there were no small courtesies, no praise, not even a grunt of acknowledgment! She was but a grain of sand in the desert, if she went absent it was doubtful whether anyone would bother to look for her ...

'You sit there like a small grey bird, mademoiselle, an English migrant who has winged its way across the ocean and landed exhausted in the alien desert.'

She stared, unable to believe him capable of speaking in a tone of amused indulgence. He had been riding earlier that morning and looked comfortably at ease in a casual shirt open at the neck and with short sleeves that left brown, sinewy forearms bare. His hair was slightly tousled, either by perplexed fingers or by the light morning breeze, and it was easy to imagine him galloping into the cool break of dawn, sitting tall in the saddle, enjoying his mastery of the most mettlesome, the most aristocratic stallion housed within the Sheikh's stables. She blinked her astonishment when, still in a moderately pleasant tone, he continued.

'I suspect, mademoiselle, that you came to my office with the intention of acting as a dove of peace, tendering an olive branch in the hope that it might ward off

the wrath you expected might fall upon your head.'
She was about to protest that his assumption was completely wrong when, in the manner of the sheikh who
never expected women to voice a viewpoint, he continued speaking. 'However, I did not demand your
presence merely to take you to task, although,' his
brows beetled, 'I must remember at some future date to
elaborate upon the folly of allowing children to recognise dissent between their elders.'

'I couldn't agree more! Nor could I find fault with
the opinions you expressed, it was simply a case of——'

'Will you please be quiet, mademoiselle, until I have
finished saying what I have to say?' Ignoring her gasp
of indignation, he went on, calmly and levelly, to as-
tound her. 'At the present time I am more concerned
about the children's safety than I am about their manners. Whispers have reached me of a coup that is
being planned, an attempt by a person in high office to
overthrow the Sheikh's regime. I am almost certain I
know the identity of the ringleader, but without proof
I cannot hope to convince the Sheikh that he is in great
danger ... especially from one as close to him as a
brother.'

Blood turned to ice in her veins. 'Zaid ...?' she whispered.

He nodded. 'You are very perceptive, mademoiselle.
As you have been so short a time in the palace, I can
only put it down to that phenomenon, feminine in-
tuition. You *were* just guessing, were you not?'

Though the question was casually put Dove could
feel his eyes raking her face and knew he was assessing
every nuance of expression. Feeing uncomfortably sus-

pect, she stammered, 'Of course! I suppose, having taken a dislike to the man on sight, I jumped to a rather obvious conclusion.'

'Another feminine trait,' he opined dryly.

When he relaxed in his chair her taut body slumped with relief. For one horrifying moment she had felt distrusted, and the experience had not been pleasant. Granted, in such a job as his, he would need to be constantly on guard, suspicious of everyone's motives, yet still she felt indignant. After all, he had gone to the lengths of travelling all the way to England in order to ascertain personally the honesty of the person chosen to be in close touch, all during the day and night, with two of the Sheikh's most priceless possessions, and not for one moment could her own honesty and integrity be questioned.

She gasped, thoughts piling one on top of the other as her train of thought was halted as if by the impact of a brick wall. Heavens! If ever he should find out that she had lied! Imagination soared into wild, uncontrollable flight as she scrabbled to remember the forms of punishment most favoured by officers commanding the tough legionnaires. Thrashing was one! Being turned out into the desert without food or water was another!

She was not aware that he had left his seat until his shadow loomed over her. Instinctively she cowered.

'*Tiens!*' he rasped. 'I did not intend to frighten you so. Here, drink this!' The rim of a glass was thrust between her teeth and when fiery liquid caught at the back of her throat she almost choked.

Spluttering, she jerked her head away. 'No! Please, I'm all right now . . .'

His disgust stung more than the brandy. 'I had hoped,' he indicted hardly, 'to enlist your help by asking you to keep your eyes and ears open for any sign, any hint, however slight, that might in some way be connected with the safety of the children in your charge. However, you can forget I mentioned the subject, mademoiselle, for obviously you are a dove not only in name but also by nature.'

# CHAPTER SIX

'HE might just as well have called me a *coward*!' Dove fumed, pacing furiously around the sitting-room of the suite that had so delighted her when she had been shown into it the previous day.

*Was it only yesterday?*

The colour scheme of dreamy pastel shades that blended delightfully, giving an impression of being surrounded by flowers, struck her as puzzling. Arabs preferred vivid colours, hot yellows, brilliant sky blues, the harsh purples, oranges and reds of the sun as it set, throwing a nocturnal cloak of coolness over burning sands.

Her bedroom was decorated mainly in green with here and there a trace of white and touches of pale yellow. Lying in bed she could imagine she was back once more in an English meadow within plucking reach of daisies and buttercups and, if she tried very hard, she could almost hear the water of a stream gurgling over stones. The bathroom was pristine white but, as if at the insistence of an Arab hand, towels, bathmats and curtains were of various shades of blue and a row of bulbous glass bottles, tapered high to the neck, bulging to their pointed stoppers with perfumed bath salts, contrasted with sapphirine beauty against stark walls.

Dove hesitated outside a door adjoining the nursery quarters listening, from force of habit, for any sound that might indicate that her charges were awake. All was quiet. She need not have bothered, for besides the guards posted constantly at either end of the passageway a maid was in attendance upon the children all during the night, ministering to them if they awoke or just sitting in readiness at the side of their beds. It had been impressed upon her that the children were never for one second to be left alone—and knowing the barbaric punishments Arabs meted out to wrongdoers, she had no doubt the girl would carry out her orders to the letter.

Last night she had been almost too tired to eat. When supper had been brought to her room she had swallowed without tasting, then crawled into bed and slept without stirring right through until morning. But tonight she felt restless, keyed up by Marc Blais's scathing remarks, so she decided that a walk in the garden might be beneficial to her peace of mind.

She had already showered and changed into a dress of fine blue wool. Having discovered that the desert night air was surprisingly chilly, she hugged a matching stole around her shoulders before making her way down to the gardens. The guard at the end of the passageway eyed her impassively as she passed him to descend the stairs. She shivered and snuggled closer into her stole. An aura of threat hung around the palace; even the floral fountain looked dejected, flowerheads drooping, drained of sap, casting petals outstanding as drops of blood on to the marble floor.

Outside a huge moon was progressing slowly across a black velvet sky. Slightly comforted, Dove noted the rise of the Milky Way over the far horizon. Here, at last, was a sight that was familiar, a twinkling reminder that home was not all that far away. Halfway along the path she halted to lift her eyes to the star-spangled sky and drew in deep breaths of mysterious, perfumed desert air.

'According to legend, Miss Grey, the stars are no more than tiny holes in a tent the Gazelle threw over the earth in an attempt to trap her lover who always left her before dawn to avoid revealing his ugliness.'

Alarmed by the sensuous, amused voice reaching out of the darkness, she gasped, 'Who's there?'

A shadow detached itself from a dark bank of shrubs. 'It is I, Zaid. Pray, do not be alarmed. I am delighted to discover that we have a common bond—you too are a lover of the night. Men of my race love the night because of its refreshing coolness, an attribute which you also possess, Miss Grey!'

She felt a prickle of fear. He too possessed the attributes of night—dark, and full of hidden danger. She forced a laugh and took a step nearer the palace. Sensing that to show fear would be as fatal as was the scent of blood to a hound, she instilled crispness into her reply. 'Darkness can deceive the senses. On a night such as this even an atheist might be tempted to believe in God.'

To her dismay, his hand shot out to detain her when she made to pass him. 'Don't go.' He smiled the lazy command.

'I must!' she protested, clutching at her stole. 'I'm feeling cold.'

Swiftly he whipped the cloak from around his shoulders and before she could move encased her within its

folds. Keeping a hand on either side of the collar, he
drew her towards him. She stifled a cry of panic, knowing that to a man such as he resistance would be considered a challenge. Contempt was her only weapon;
she used it like a sword, sharp and cutting.

'I am no *houriyeh* and I very much resent being
treated as one. Please let me go, or I shall be forced to
complain to your brother, the Sheikh!'

Unmoved by her threat, Zaid pulled her closer,
transfixing her with a fanatical gleam. 'What is your
melting price, maiden of the snow? We Arabs are well
aware that you English girls come out East in search of
gold, so gold you shall have. Name your price.'

Dove discovered deep within her a hidden well of
temper that years of tranquil living had left undisturbed. It surged into life, a great flood of rage that
rushed through her veins, sending a sparkle into her
eyes and a tide of angry colour into her cheeks. Her
lips were about to frame the first of a furious spurt of
words when a voice crackled through the darkness.

'The woman is mine, Zaid. She is not for sale.'

Dove had never imagined she would actually welcome the sight of the dark presence that loomed out of
the shadows, but as Zaid's hands loosened she squirmed
out of the cloak and ran towards the tall figure ominously waiting.

'Monsieur Blais!' she choked, forgetful of pride, and
was clutched by hands that dug unmercifully into her
waist.

Zaid stared, obviously astounded, then curled his lip
into an unpleasant, meaningful leer. 'By Allah, we live
as brothers yet keep counsel as if we were but passing

strangers. This woman must indeed be special if she has aroused your interest, for your views of the opposite sex are well known: *Today the fire, tomorrow the ashes*. Has that not always been your belief?' He threw back his head and laughed; a sound echoing with triumph. 'Four things impair the strength of man— sin, starvation, privation, and sex! At last,' his glittering eyes fell upon Dove, who shivered even in the protection of the hawk, 'you have betrayed a weakness, friend Marc! The first three leave you unmoved, but this last,' with a nod he indicated Dove, 'could prove to be your downfall.'

With a stealth Dove found disconcerting he disappeared into the darkness. For seconds she did not move—did not want to move away from the hard arm that represented safety even though fingers of steel were inflicting punishment upon her waist. When he pushed her aside she felt deserted, the gap between them an alien no-man's-land.

'Thank you ...' she stammered, 'for coming to my rescue. For a while there I suffered a few anxious moments.'

'You amaze me!' He expelled a hard angry breath.

She peered through the darkness, seeking a clue to his anger in a face made even more satanic by the shroud of night.

'I warned you, did I not, of the consequences of leading on men of volatile temperament, yet you deliberately set out to ensnare the most dangerous of all. Zaid can give you riches, mademoiselle, but are you sure you are prepared to endure what will be demanded in return? The man is a *barbarian*,' he hissed, clutching her by the arm to stress with painful emphasis, 'a monster who would show no mercy to a young idiot such as yourself!' He released her suddenly, retreating as if from someone defiled, and charged with impatient contempt, 'You deserve to be punished for your greed! Why I bothered to intercede I'll never know ...'

The meaning behind his words struck her like a thunderclap. 'You can't *possibly* be thinking....! You surely don't imagine that I *encouraged* Zaid!'

'You surely don't imagine,' he mimicked with infuriating derision, 'that I am simpleton enough to believe that you did not?'

Completely stumped for words, Dove glared into his implacable face, knowing protests would be useless. He was a woman-hater with a mind as scarred as his face, a man whose allegiance in any conflict between the sexes would inevitably lie with the male.

'You really are convinced that I'm mercenary,' she finally faltered.

'And unscrupulous. And scheming. In fact, mademoiselle, I know that you are a young woman of very determined character who will not hesitate to employ deceit to further your own ends!' She winced, feeling his barb landing uncomfortably near to the truth. Grimly, he continued, 'The initial purpose for your presence here was to ease some of my responsibility towards the children, so allowing me more time for other pressing duties. As you have turned out to be just an added aggravation, I think the best solution would be for you to return to England immediately. Naturally, you will return the money that was advanced to you, less a percentage as compensation for the small amount of inconvenience you have been caused.'

'You mean ... I'm being dismissed?'

'I would not have put it so bluntly,' he shrugged, 'but yes, in effect, you are.'

Dove's newly-found temper erupted. She had done nothing to deserve such treatment. They had entered into an agreement which he had insisted she must keep, yet he seemingly did not consider that the rules laid down were applicable to himself. Even through the darkness her defiance was apparent, as jutting her chin, she countered, 'Sorry to disappoint you, monsieur, but as I no longer have the money I can't return it. Whether you like it or not I shall have to stay ... Unless,' in her temper she resorted to impudence, 'you decide to write off the debt, in which case I shall begin packing my things?'

'Not on your gold-digging life!' She bit back a cry of pain when fingers like claws dug into her upper arm. Coiled-up fury emanated from his fingertips, an urge to punish which, had she been another man, would have terminated in a blow. Yet had he struck her she would not have winced so much as she did from his disgusted glare. 'If that is the case, then you must stay. But don't be too swift to congratulate yourself on your cleverness. One year spent in the desert can seem like ten—it shall be my pleasure to ensure that yours resembles an eternal hell!'

Dove crept upstairs to her room feeling shaken, battered by a storm of emotion, and collapsed on to the bed. Marc Blais meant every word, of that she felt certain, and who was better qualified to inflict both mental and physical torture than a man whose job it had been in the recent past to break the spirit of tough legionnaires, mercenaries, men of fortune, and some simply out-and-out rogues. The prospect of spending even one more day in his company was terrifying. Their enmity had now been openly declared—what armour had she against brute strength, against a thirst for vengeance? She closed her eyes and tried to picture the worst that could happen, but all she could see of her future was an opaque surface reflecting her own haunted eyes, woebegone mouth, and pale, solemn face.

The following morning, depressed and heavy-eyed from lack of sleep, she found it difficult to keep irritation from her voice when the children, deciding they had been on their best behaviour long enough, showed signs of tantrums and, in Salim's case, downright disobedience. The breakfast table, when they had finished eating, resembled a battlefield, and when the clash of wills threatened to continue right throughout the morning Dove decided wearily that she had stood enough.

'We must find some place where they can work off their surplus energy, Alya. Collect a few of their toys, we'll take them into the garden to play.'

'Can I take my scooter and ride it up and down the paths, Miss Grey?' Bibi pleaded.

'If you wish,' she nodded, relieved to see a smile replacing Bibi's mutinous expression.

'Me ... Panda!' Salim was not asking permission, merely stating his intention, and she had to smile at the sight of a small boy tugging towards the door a giant panda almost as big as himself.

'Why not let me carry Panda?' she suggested lightly,

foreseeing disaster should the toddler insist upon struggling down the stairs with his cumbersome burden. For a moment he glared, then, deciding he had been asked rather than commanded, he handed it over with a cherubic smile traced with a charm which in later years, Dove thought wryly, would win him anything he coveted. But then most Arabs had a practised charm. Unlike a certain Frenchman they could, if their mood allowed it, bestow almost poetic praise. Thrusting all thoughts of Marc Blais to the back of her mind, she ushered the children downstairs and out into the garden.

The two guards detached themselves from their positions outside the nursery and followed them outside, where they stood with arms folded, keeping the children within their line of vision. At first their presence was an embarrassment to Dove—but then the children began demanding her attention and soon she was able to forget that the two sentries existed.

They played together for almost an hour, then, as gradually the children became absorbed in their own little worlds, she relaxed into a chair Alya had positioned under the shade of a tree and accepted gratefully the glass of lemonade that was poured for her.

'Mmm ... delicious!' She smiled her appreciation. 'Life in the desert can be monotonous, but it does have compensations.'

Bibi sped past on her scooter, exercising her lungs as well as her limbs with yells of delighted pleasure, so Salim, who was never slow to imitate, picked up his toy drum and began strutting around the lawn plying his sticks with noisy joy. Dove leant back in her seat with a relieved smile. Clearly the novelty of even this small amount of freedom had gone to their heads; another hour or so of such activity would leave them pleasantly tired and far more amenable to discipline.

'We must make an hour or two in the garden part of our daily routine,' she told Alya, watching through half-closed lids as Bibi negotiated the flower beds, then raced to scatter a flock of birds busy pecking in her path.

'Miss Grey . . .!' Alya drew her attention to a young maidservant hovering anxiously behind her chair.

'Yes?' Dove smiled at the girl.

With downcast eyes, the girl intoned, 'Mariam, my mistress, has sent me with a request that the children should be taken indoors—their noise is disturbing her rest.'

'Damn!' The girl could not have heard the softly breathed expletive, but the expression on Dove's face caused her to back away. Feeling slightly ashamed, Dove apologised immediately. Seething though she was, she had no right to vent her anger on the girl. 'I'm sorry,' she told her gently. 'Please tell your mistress that I shall do as she asks.' Then, bracing herself for argument, she called out to the children:

'Gather up your toys, it's time to go indoors!'

As expected, her request was met with a chorus of dissent.

'I want to stay here!' Bibi wailed.

'No!' Salim defied her, then in case she had not heard stressed each following syllable with a thump upon his drum. 'No, no, no-o-o-o!'

Drastic measures were called for. Dove could quite

easily have demanded obedience in a no-nonsense manner which would probably have reduced the pair of them to tears, but her sympathies were definitely with them, so she searched her mind for some source of physical pleasure that could be enjoyed out of door yet in comparative silence.

Her flash of inspiration came coloured bright blue— a blue-tiled swimming pool, shallow at one end and deep at the other, positioned far enough away from their mother's quarters to render their activities noise-less.

Brightly she turned to the children. 'How would you like a swim?' she asked, then waited for their joyful reaction.

Bibi looked doubtful. 'Are we allowed?' she quizzed. Salim was blankly staring as if the suggestion held no meaning for him.

'Why ever not?' Dove replied with assurance. 'The pool seems never to be occupied—each time I've passed it's been deserted. Come, Alya shall hunt out your bathing suits while I look for mine.'

Eager to participate in this new adventure, the child-ren scattered up to the nursery with Alya tagging slowly behind. Dove went straight to her own room to forage for one of the swimsuits she had included in her lug-gage. In mere seconds she had undressed and donned a crisp apple green two-piece, comprising minute bikini pants and matching strapless top that clung to her curves like strategically-placed fig leaves. A full-length towelling robe, zipped from neck to hem, completed the outfit which, as she hurried into the nursery, brought a look of admiration to Alya's face.

'What's wrong? Why aren't the children ready?'

Alya's puzzled frown returned. 'I'm sorry, Miss Grey, but the children do not usually wear clothes when they bathe.'

Dove looked doubtful. 'Don't they? I suppose, considering their tender years, a bathing suit is hardly necessary, but,' she frowned, 'as Monsieur Blais keeps reminding me that Arabs are rather straight-laced, I think they'd better wear something, just to be on the safe side.'

She could not understand, as they made their way back to the swimming pool, why the fact that Bibi was wearing only cotton briefs under her sunsuit should send her into paroxysms of giggles or why Salim should keep attempting to tug his skimpy tee-shirt down past a few inches of bright red underpants. However, once they were frolicking in the shallows with the enjoyment of baby seals, Dove's mind cleared of all but the pleasurable anticipation of her first swim beneath a warm desert sun. Eagerly she unzipped her robe and let it slip to the ground before plunging in, blissfully unaware as she swam, dived and floated on the surface of water soft and cool as cream against her skin, that Alya, after one horrified gasp, had covered her eyes with her hands and run panic-stricken in the direction of the palace.

She was floating dreamily on the surface of the water, slim as a willow stripped of all but three essential leaves, when she heard a great splash, then seconds later a shadow loomed, blotting out the sun. When a vice closed around her waist, lifting her clear from the water, she was too startled to scream, and the roughness

with which she was bundled into her robe, thrown
across a hard shoulder, then whisked towards the
palace, made it difficult even to fight for breath.

In an incredibly short space of time she was deposited, dripping wet, inside her room. She winced as a
violent kick crashed shut the door and extended a
trembling hand behind her back, searching for help to
support her trembling limbs. She made contact with a
chair and sank into it, then forced herself to meet the
eyes of the man standing glowering down at her, arms
tightly folded across his chest.

'*Idiote!*' he spat. '*Stupide!*'

Her shaking became uncontrollable. This time he
was not merely angry, he was in a towering rage! Common sense bade her remain silent until he had regained
control, but a surge of resentment was her undoing.
Rising to her feet, she stormed:

'I'd like an explanation of your extraordinary behaviour, monsieur. Never in my life——'

'The life you came very near to losing!' he interrupted grimly. If he had yelled she would not have
listened, but the terse warning would not be ignored.

'What do you mean?' she gasped.

'I mean that women have been beheaded for dis-
playing less of their bodies than you were a few
moments ago. Modesty is a much prized virtue in this
country—an Arab won't even remove his headdress
until he is in the privacy of his own quarters, so, understandably, mixed bathing is strictly forbidden.'

'Mixed bathing? You mean the *children* ... ?'

'The children, yes. Also, in the eyes of his people
Salim's importance is second only to his father's. By

cavorting almost nude in front of him you left yourself open to a charge of attempted corruption.'

'*Cavorting? Corruption?*' Her voice soared high with incredulity. 'Oh, please, monsieur, don't insult my intelligence!'

With one stride he closed the gap between them. Savagely he grabbed her by the shoulders, flicking scorn like a whip. 'If you will not listen to words of reason, mademoiselle, then you leave me no choice but to demonstrate. *This* is a sample of what you must expect if you insist upon inviting rape!'

# CHAPTER SEVEN

NUMBLY, Dove picked up the scraps of green from the floor, dropped them into a drawer and closed it tight, hoping to forget their very existence. What, back home in England, would have been considered an innocuous bathing suit had become, owing to the actions of one man, representative of lust, savagery, and utter debasement. She had been the innocent that had thought no evil; she had suffered the consequence of such naïveté.

She shuddered, took a step towards the bathroom, then paused. She had to be sensible. Three times she had showered, had stood for what seemed hours, tears mingled with spray, trying to scrub away the imprint of cruel hands from a body of which, it seemed, no part had been left untouched. He had set out to punish, and the punishment had been characteristically severe. One thing he had taught her—how to hate, an emotion she had never before experienced. She now knew it well. It had sprung to life the moment his lips had savaged her mouth and had had time to grow and strengthen while, without tenderness or compassion, he had debased her to the level of an Arabian *houriyeh*. Then he had left her, a quivering nerveless wreck, thrashed yet physically unmarked, incapable of answering his derisive farewell with anything but a gasping sob.

Her hand closed around an ornamental dagger, one of a display laid out upon a shelf. If only it had been within reach when she had most needed it—the moment a scarred mouth had smiled with a negligence that in itself had been insulting, and commented: 'You have much to learn, grey dove. Zaid was prepared to barter, but he would have felt immeasurably cheated had he received a snowdrop in exchange for his gold.'

A rap sounded upon the door and the dagger she was holding fell with a clatter to the floor. She fought for composure, but her voice sounded highly strung when she called out: 'Who's there?'

'It is Alya!'

'Come in if you must!' She walked across to the window, keeping her back turned in case the maid should read shame emblazoned across her expressive face. 'What do you want, Alya?' she enquired in a flat, expressionless voice.

'Mistress Mariam wishes to speak with you.'

Dove leant her hot forehead against the cool bars striping the window. 'All right,' she sighed, 'I'll be along presently.'

'But, Miss Grey!' Alya sounded scandalised, 'my mistress awaits you now.'

Dove drew in a deep breath. Nerves were thudding through her body, her eyes felt hot, her pulses were leaping, her skin crawled. Painfully, she swallowed, then with deceiving calmness assured the maid, 'In five minutes, then, just time enough for me to slip out of this dressing-gown and into a dress.'

Mariam was in her customary position, stretched out with languid ease upon a divan. Dove shrank from the curiosity in eyes that roved her face and figure as she slowly advanced into the room. Colour flamed her cheeks. It was as if Mariam was aware of her humiliation and, in the hope of enlivening a dull hour, was prepared to probe and gloat.

Yet puzzlement was the overriding nuance in her voice when, after a thorough examination of Dove's pale, haunted face she commented, 'It amazes me the way your English timidity charms the men of my race. Zaid's interest is perhaps not so unusual, for he is always in search of novelty, but Marc's passions run fathoms deep and are consequently far more difficult to arouse. I had imagined he would choose a woman possessed of fire equal to his own.' When angry colour stained Dove's cheeks Mariam's interest quickened. Could it be that she had misjudged the deceptively mild English miss? Marc was noted for his shrewd assessment of character; it was just possible that he had been clever enough to recognise depths which remained hidden to all but the most perceptive.

'I resent being classed as anyone's *woman*!' Dove's tone was as heated as her cheeks. 'No man can lay claim upon me—not Zaid, and certainly not Monsieur Blais.'

Mariam shrugged. The ways of Western women were beyond her. Waving Dove towards a chair, she countered dryly, 'It is pointless to shelter behind a smokescreen of secrecy when everyone is aware that you have found favour in Marc's eyes. From the lips of Rahma, my husband, I heard of the feud that has sprung to life between Zaid and Marc. Those two have balanced on the knife-edge of dislike for years, now rivalry has toppled them into a state of bitter enmity. Zaid's appeal to my husband that his desire for you should take precedence over Marc's was turned down.

Though he is my husband's brother and holds a senior post in his administration Marc is nearer to my husband's heart.'

She yawned delicately, then snuggled into a more comfortable position. Long hours could be shortened by gossip, especially when one's listener was staring wide-eyed with astonishment. 'Naturally, Zaid was furious when my husband insisted that if Marc wanted you then you were to be his. There is a bond between them,' she mused, 'that transcends even family loyalty. It was forged when, as young men, they joined the Foreign Legion in search of adventure. During their years together they suffered much hardship, fought many battles, the details of which are known only to them. The one secret they could not keep was the fact that my husband would not be alive today were it not for Marc. The scar on his face serves as a constant reminder to my husband that he owes his life to his friend!'

When Dove made a small gurgling sound in her throat Mariam paused, but when the question she was expecting did not come, she continued, 'I know that it has troubled my husband greatly that he had been unable to find a way of rewarding Marc. Owing to a family inheritance, he has no need of money, and the fact that he has undertaken the task of protecting our children places us even deeper in his debt. You must therefore be able to understand, Miss Grey, how happy my husband is to grant this one small favour to his friend. At this very moment the palace kitchens are in a frenzy of preparation for the betrothal feast which has been planned for tonight.'

'Betrothal feast?' Dove repeated stupidly, wondering if she had misheard.

'Yes,' Mariam nodded, 'isn't it exciting! As a rule, only men are present at such feasts, but as you are not of our race my husband has decided to adopt the British custom of allowing women guests.'

Feeling trapped in some hideous nightmare, Dove jumped to her feet and exclaimed in a passion of resentment, 'You must all be mad! Every one of you must be clear off your heads if you imagine you can force me, a British subject, to fall in with your archaic customs! I hate Marc Blais! He's the last man in the world I'd consider marrying—even if he were to wish it, which I'm sure he does not, for the only emotion we share is one of mutual dislike!'

'Come now, Miss Grey,' Mariam trilled, 'you need not pretend to me!'

'*Pretend?*' Dove almost choked. 'Who's pretending?'

Mariam smiled as she glimpsed for a second a hint of the fiery passion she had decided was essential to Marc's happiness. 'You will discover, Miss Grey, that your wishes are of no consequence to the sons of Adam who rule this kingdom. The day you became part of his household you became one of my husband's possessions. If he wishes you to marry Marc you will do so. But don't worry,' she soothed, 'before my own marriage I had not even seen Rahma's face, yet love came to me—as it will to you.'

Dove felt the fatalism of the East pressing down upon her. Mariam spoke as if her betrothal to Marc Blais were almost a *fait accompli*. She experienced the panic of a bird trapped behind bars and had to press a hand to a heart reacting with the frenzy of fluttering wings. She drew a deep breath, willing the panic to subside, and after a few seconds was able with comparative calmness to enunciate slowly:

'I don't think you understood what I said. I want no part of your planned charade—not even to please Sheikh Rahma will I become betrothed to that beast!'

Mariam's eyebrows rose. 'Marc, a beast...?'

Emphatically, Dove nodded. 'A savage, unfeeling monster!'

Mariam, who was a couple of years younger than Dove, shot a glance from eyes holding the wisdom of age, then gave an understanding nod. 'It is clear that you are a virgin who feels her modesty has been violated.' When Dove winced, Mariam's lips curled into a half-smile. Sympathetically she urged, 'Virile men are the greatest lovers of virtue. As a maiden you would be wise to preserve yours, but you must cast it aside once you are wed, for virtue can become an ice-cold barrier in a warm bed.'

Dove's aggravation was so great she stamped her foot. 'The lecture is hardly applicable. I have no intention of sharing a bed, warm or otherwise, with Monsieur Blais.'

Suddenly Mariam lost patience. 'You are an ungrateful girl,' she scolded. 'Many women have yearned over the man you scorn. You do not deserve him, and I shall tell my husband so. Meanwhile, I advise you to go to your room and think carefully before giving your final decision. If you continue with your ungrateful attitude my husband might, in his anger, turn you over to his brother Zaid, and if this should be your fate then I shall shudder for you, for all of thirty nights and thirty days. You condemn Marc as a beast, yet after one night of Zaid's company he will appear to you to compare favourably with one of your angelic saints.'

The thread of certainty running through Mariam's words sent a chill of fear chasing up Dove's spine. Hot words cooled upon her tongue, fire drained from her cheeks, leaving them colourless as snow. Mariam nodded, well pleased. 'Go now, Miss Grey, dwell long and deeply on what I have said, remembering always that though the hawk's talons hold fast the claws of a fox know only how to rend ...'

Back in her own suite Dove discovered to her disgust that she was unable to stop shivering. She prowled the room, berating herself for allowing the mutterings of an ignorant Arab girl to cloud her judgment. Subconsciously imitating the superstitions of the East, she rummaged in a drawer, searching for her passport, and when she had found it, clutched it like a talisman against evil.

'They dare not carry out such threats against one of Her Majesty's subjects,' she decided, staring down at the small leather booklet with its impressive gold seal. Then her spirits plummeted. The nearest British Embassy was miles away, but even if it were not she knew she would receive very little sympathy from diplomats grown cynical in attitude towards girls who ignored warnings and flew East in search of wealth. 'Western nations,' Jennifer had pointed out, 'are heavily dependent upon Arab oil and are therefore most reluctant to offend powerful rulers of oil-producing States.' Too late, Dove wished she had heeded her advice.

After an hour of ceaseless prowling courage came to her aid. She sat down and forced herself to reason calmly. It seemed she was destined to become the spoils of a war between two men whose mutual antipathy had for years been held in check, only to erupt upon her arrival. She therefore had the choice of siding with a man she hated or with one she feared. At least she had no illusions about Marc Blais's feelings; the emotions she aroused in him ran the gamut from impatience to contempt. This betrothal had been forced upon him by Zaid's attempt to pull rank and he must now be feeling as frustrated and angry about the situation as she was herself. That, at least, was some small consolation.

Zaid, on the other hand, had demonstrated by both looks and insinuation that he coveted her body. Satiated by a surfeit of dusky beauties, his appetite had been whetted by what he had described as her pale, distant delicacy. The mere idea of his dark, sensuous hands upon her body so revolted her that she cringed.

Some time later, when Mariam sent a servant to discover whether or not she had come to her senses, she replied with a quivering Yes, and was thereupon instructed to begin dressing for the feast which was scheduled to begin in a couple of hours' time. This instruction she ignored. Marc Blais must take her as she was or leave her, mercifully, alone. A quick shower and change into her plainest dress was all the effort she intended.

The dress she chose was simple to the point of severity—white, with a small sleeve, a scooped-out neckline, and tailored to fit an incredibly slim waistline. Its freezing whiteness was reflected in her small pointed features, and as she stepped out of her bedroom into the passageway, straight into the path of Marc Blais, he was reminded of the flower to which he had likened her—the delicate snowdrop that fought its way to life against great odds then strove with head bowed to combat stormy elements.

'Mariam tells me she has put you in the picture?' His voice was clamped with irritation, yet as his eyes roved her face a glint appeared which told her he was remembering their last encounter.

Embarrassment goaded her into a jibe. 'She has. As I understand the situation, the Sheikh is eager to reward you for services rendered, so I'm being coerced into a betrothal to a man who is incapable of finding a woman for himself!'

The insult made no impact. Reaching out, he clamped her chin between two forceful fingers and jerked her head upwards so that she was bound to meet his eyes. 'A lamb to the slaughter, is that how you wish to see yourself? Rather than admit to being foolish, headstrong, and completely without scruples, you adopt a pose of injured innocence. I wish I had your imagination, mademoiselle, then I, too, could pretend—that you did not exist!'

He was striding down the passageway before she managed to subdue her sense of outrage. Words it was too late to utter spilled to her lips—arrogant, brutal, churlish, conceited—each adjective was applicable. Then, when reason was about to snap, bitter humour came to her aid. Shortly she was to take part in a mock betrothal ceremony which she, at least, did not

consider binding. How much worse it would have been
had she been contemplating marriage to the man, to
speak vows which in all honesty would have had to
read: 'I, Dove, take thee, Marc, to be my unlawful
husband, to hate, loathe and despise from this day forward, until death us do part ...!'

She felt strange seated at the foot of a low table surrounded by giggling wives who were seemingly over-
whelmed by the unaccustomed honour of joining their
husbands at the table. Dove was the only one unveiled.
Some of the elderly male Arabs were obviously em-
barrassed by this omission, for after one quick glance
they studiously avoided looking her way.

Marc Blais—her lord and master, she cynically dub-
bed him—was seated to the right of Sheikh Rahma
who was presiding at the head of the table. Zaid was
seated on his left, and as the very sedate dinner proceeded the Sheikh divided his attention scrupulously
between the two men while, in the Arab way, they
munched solidly through the courses until their
stomachs were full. Only water was served with the
meal, which probably accounted for the fact that little
laughter enlivened the men's conversation.

The meal was fairly simple, but Dove was in trouble
from the very first course. After everyone's hands had
been washed, Rahma began the meal by plunging his
spoon into a large tureen of soup and the rest of the
men followed suit, spoons plying between one tureen
and several mouths with considerable effect. The
women were served separately, and after an initial
fastidious shrinking from the thought of sharing a dish
with several other mouths Dove tried a spoonful of

the dark green soup and found it delicious.

The second course, however, was a nightmare. Meat dishes were carried in, lamb grilled over charcoal and set upon beds of vegetables; meat balls and kebabs, skewers of grilled meat, chunks of lamb alternating with lumps of minced meat, set upon dishes of brown beans flavoured with garlic, dressed with oil, and flavoured with lemon. Her female companions were shy yet eager to initiate her into the proper method of transferring food to mouth from out of a communal dish.

'Take a piece of bread, so!' Mariam demonstrated. 'Hold it to the edge of the dish with the thumb and first two fingers of your right hand. The left hand is never used at meals except in cases of extreme necessity. Then draw a portion of meat upon your bread and convey it to your mouth.' The operation, when Mariam carried it out, was really clean and tidy, but Dove entertained a giggling audience for almost five minutes while she chased a piece of meat around the rim of the serving dish before finally scooping it onto her piece of bread.

Gradually, with the aid of many helpful suggestions, she became more dexterous in the art, choosing only the most manageable-sized pieces of meat and avoiding the haricot beans done in oil that had to be conveyed gingerly to the mouth and deposited well inside the lips. The sight of numerous fingers dipping into the beans, depositing them into mouths, then returning once more to the same dish was slightly nauseating.

It was a relief when the sweet course arrived. Bowls

of fruit already decorated the tables, together with jugs of some sweet drink that seemed mostly to be composed of water and raisins. Arabs were notoriously sweet-toothed, but Dove was surprised at the selection offered. She dithered between a choice of delicate pastries stuffed with dates and coated with powdered sugar, pancakes drenched in syrup and served with nuts, almonds and thick clotted cream, then finally opted for a cigar-shaped cake made of paper-thin pastry, stuffed with an almond filling, then dipped in syrup. Her companions' amusement at her choice was explained when with a smile Mariam told her:

'An apt choice, Miss Grey. The name of the sweet you have chosen is "bride's fingers."'

Tension had left her and she was almost beginning to enjoy herself when, after a final washing of hands, the servants cleared the tables and an expectant hush fell over the assembly. 'Prepare yourself,' Mariam whispered. 'The ceremony is about to begin. You are very honoured. Rahma, my husband, has taken it upon himself to deputise for your father during the betrothal rites. He has already bartered with Marc for your dowry—a handsome sum, more than ample to cover the cost of your trousseau.'

*Already she had been bought and paid for!*

When a man detached himself from the group at the head of the table and began advancing towards her she knew that the moment she had been dreading had arrived. She had assured herself philosophically that the betrothal ceremony meant nothing, merely a charade that had to be played out for the amusement of a people of simple, childlike intellect. But as she was escorted amidst a solemn hush to where Rahma and Marc were waiting a sea of grave faces impressed an importance upon the occasion which would not be shrugged off.

Marc's serious expression did not help to lighten her fears and as she took her place next to him, in front of Sheikh Rahma, the aura of solemnity was magnified when, in a devout voice quivering with feeling, the Sheikh began magnifying God, invoking blessings upon the Prophet, then embarked upon what seemed endless passages from the Koran. Dove did not once look towards her supposed prospective bridegroom, but felt him standing stiffly to attention right throughout the religious part of the ceremony. Only once, by accident, did their eyes meet, and that was when Marc was requested to hand over the dowry that had been agreed. The huge bundle of notes he placed upon a tray held out in front of him caused her an amazed gasp, to which he in turn responded with a twist of his scarred, cynical mouth before he moved away to take a seat opposite Rahma, her deputy father, and grasped his hands.

A tall Arab stepped forward to throw a handkerchief over their joined hands and Dove, abandoned in the crowd, feeling almost superfluous to the ceremony, began to shake as Rahma solemnly intoned:

'I betroth to thee my daughter Dove, the virgin, for a dowry of one thousand pounds.'

She felt she had wandered into a world of unreality, the dim faceless crowd a mirage, the deeply religious ceremony an hallucination. Her senses reeled, she felt sick and faint, then terribly afraid when, through the pounding in her ears, she heard Marc's crisp, decisive reply:

'I accept her betrothal from thee ...'

# CHAPTER EIGHT

*'Don't cry out!'* Dove was startled from out of a rest-less sleep when the words hissed into her ear. The com-mand was superfluous, for the man leaning across her bed had his hand pressed over her mouth to stifle a startled scream. 'Get dressed, then quickly and as silently as possible prepare the children for a trip into the desert.'

Her wide, startled eyes stared into the face of Marc Blais. He looked grim, the scar, which she was begin-ning to use as a barometer of his feelings, a jagged white line outstanding against a tense jaw.

'What's wrong?' she gasped.

'There's no time for explanations,' he replied, his impatience evident, 'the children are in danger and must be removed from the palace as quickly as possible. I'll be back in five minutes—be ready!'

As soon as her confused mind registered the fact that he had gone she scrambled out of bed, donned a pair of slacks and a thick jumper and ran to the nursery quarters. A frightened maid had already roused the children, who had obviously been cautioned to remain silent, an order they were in no mood to disobey as, in a state of semi-wakefulness, they were bundled into warm clothing. Dove had just finished fastening a hood over Salim's head when a tall, cloaked figure ap-peared in the doorway. Her heart leapt with fear.

Instinctively, she pushed the children behind her, protecting them with her body against the man approaching with silent, cat-like tread.

'You are ready? Good! Now follow behind me as closely and as silently as possible.'

With a shock of relief she recognised the voice of Marc Blais. Never before had she seen him wearing Arab dress, and the impact was such that even in that moment of drama she registered the ease with which the black burnous settled upon his shoulders, and the way the roped headdress complemented dark features etched with an arrogance that was the hallmark of men who prided themselves on being direct descendants of Adam.

With a thumping heart and dry mouth she guided the still drowsy children in his wake, the seriousness of the exercise emphasised by the manner in which the two guards combined forces, with rifles at the ready, to cover their retreat along the passageway and down a flight of stairs leading to the rear courtyard where the bulk of a Land Rover loomed out of the darkness. In response to Marc's imperious nod Dove scrambled inside and as each child was handed over she settled them into the back seat, one either side. They snuggled close, then with the blissful innocence of untroubled minds promptly fell asleep.

As Marc slipped behind the wheel and turned the key in the ignition the crack of a rifle shot resounded from within the palace and as he pressed his foot against the accelerator Dove heard, above the roar of the engine, return fire rising above an hysterical babble of voices. The sound reacted upon Marc like a spur.

Abandoning caution, he pressed his foot down hard and sent the Land Rover racing out of the courtyard, along the drive, then through wide-open gates which were immediately clanged shut once they had made their escape into the open desert. Within minutes the outline of the palace was swallowed up by darkness, then it was as if they had cast off from port to sail an uncharted ocean of sand. There was no moon to soften the outlines of dunes that reared either side of them, dark bulks rising and falling like the waves of a storm-tossed sea under a night sky studded with huge stars bright as diamonds. The air was sharp and cold.

'Here, wrap these blankets around you! In a couple of hours we'll reach an Army post where we'll get a meal and load up with supplies before moving into the interior.'

Sensing from his slightly relaxed tone that some of the tension had left him, Dove ventured to ask, 'Would you please explain the need for this extraordinary escapade? Did you have to disturb the children from their beds at such an hour?'

She knew she sounded indignant, but for the life of her she could think of no valid reason for such melodrama, so was completely unprepared for the shock of his reply.

'The choice was one of either leaving them to sleep or abandoning them to the mercy of their uncle Zaid, who would have not the slightest compunction in ordering that their throats should be cut.'

Her heart skipped a beat. 'Surely you're exaggerating?' she protested weakly.

'Zaid, though he is their uncle, and their father's

brother, did not hesitate to plot a coup to enable him to win the sheikhdom. As this cannot possibly come to pass while Rahma and his heir still live, you must draw your own conclusions.'

'But I imagined the Sheikh's followers were loyal to a man,' she almost pleaded.

'The majority of them are,' he confirmed, 'but in the East, as in the West, the loyalty of some can be bought with gold. Zaid has been generous with his promises. I have been aware for some time that something was afoot, but as Rahma was reluctant to believe his brother capable of such treachery my hands were tied. I did, however, warn those whom I knew to be loyal to be on their guard. Also, I placed spies amongst the enemy, and it was one of these who warned me that the coup was planned to begin tonight.'

'But what about the Sheikh? Won't he be taken completely by surprise?'

'I doubt it,' he replied with reassuring confidence. 'Rahma has lived for so many years in the shadow of death and danger I would question whether, even now, he could sleep without one eye open and the comforting prick of a dagger against his thigh.'

She shuddered. In a few succinct sentences Marc had portrayed the essential characteristics of a Legionnaire, a man who trusted no one, who flirted with death and laughed at danger. A man who learned his barbarity from the dreaded outlaws of the desert whom it was his duty to subdue, tribes that raided and pillaged the caravans of peaceful merchants, who plundered, killed and raped not simply for gain but for sheer, lustful pleasure. How thin a line separated the assassin from the executioner? Legionnaires were notoriously hard, embittered men, devoid of mercy. She was alone in the desert except for two helpless children, with just such a man!

Dawn was breaking when, on the far horizon, Dove saw the outline of a mosque rising above lines of tents and a scattering of smart new bungalows. Marc braked the Land Rover outside a double line of blancoed stones that marked the entrance to a guardroom from which a private of the desert patrol—part soldiers, part police—stepped out to meet them. Their arrival must have been prearranged, for when the private escorted them to the office of Major Yasin, the commanding officer's welcome was warm but unsurprised.

'So, Marc, what you feared has come to pass?'

'Unfortunately, yes. Though I have no fear for Rahma's safety, I dared take no chances with the lives of his children. I would welcome your help, Yasin, to remove them as far as possible from the sphere of Zaid's influence.'

The major nodded, his face grave. 'Tell me what you require, my friend. Needless to say, whatever you want shall be yours.'

'Thank you.' Marc almost smiled. 'Then perhaps while we are having a meal you could arrange to have camels mustered and supplies prepared—and also,' he paused to sweep a look over Dove and the children, 'as there is no knowing into how many tribes Zaid's corruption has penetrated, some Arab garments that will act as a disguise until we reach Bedouins within whose camp the children will be well protected.'

It was amazing, Dove reflected as she helped Salim

and Bibi into voluminous garments, how easily children could adapt circumstances, however hazardous, into an enjoyable game. Now wide awake, they were intensely excited by the adventure. Salim, especially, pranced about in his Bedou garments as if his sheltered upbringing belonged in a long-distant past and only here in the desert was he completely at home. As they ran outside laughing, to seek Marc's approval, Dove looked dubiously at the garments provided for herself—a shapeless shift that fell to her ankles, with long sleeves reaching down to her wrists, a matching cloak, and a long scarf, yards long, to wrap around her head. As they looked far from new and, she suspected, they were not very clean, she slipped them over the clothes she was already wearing. She was winding the scarf around her head when Marc Blais stepped inside the room that had been placed at her disposal. Without a word of apology for his abrupt entrance, he thrust out a hand containing a jar of brown, glutinous paste.

'Here, rub this into any part of your skin left uncovered. Don't worry, the dye will wash off; it is pointless to don Arab dress without covering up that pale complexion.'

'Must I?' The paste looked revolting, a jar of liquid mud.

'You must,' he asserted with a glint that told her that argument would be useless. 'Come here, as you have no mirror I'd better help you with it.'

It took a great deal of control to subdue the distaste she felt when for the second time she endured his touch. But his fingers were completely dispassionate as he rubbed the dye into cheeks, brow, eyelids and chin, paying particular attention to the areas around her mouth. When he had finished her face and turned his attention to her neck she swallowed hard and dug fingernails deep into her palms to control the suspicion of a tremor.

His fingers, for some unknown reason, became gentler, smoothing the ointment into the soft hollow of her throat with movements that were almost caressing. She wanted to jerk away, to escape the memory of a mouth that had savaged where his fingers now smoothed. His expression had become preoccupied, as if he too were remembering, perhaps regretting, inflicting a bruise.

To retreat would be to admit defeat, so she remained very still while silently hating the memory of his brutal treatment, of the cruel mouth that had pressed scarred contempt upon her own, of the way he had shocked her out of a state of innocent naïveté and left her vitally aware of her own womanhood!

Suddenly he looked into her eyes and smiled, the derisive half-twist of the lips she had come to detest.

'I can almost feel your skin crawling when I touch you. Your revulsion rises like a wall between us. What did I do that was so shocking? I punished you, yes,' the smile became a fully-fledged sneer, 'but I could have gone further—much further. Western girls demand much of their suitors and in my chastisement of you I did not exceed what is expected of a man in these liberated days. In other words, mademoiselle, you still have your virginity—you note I pay you the compliment of assuming that that state existed upon your arrival here—but if you have not, then it was certainly not I who penetrated the veil.'

There was only one way to relieve her humiliation, one possible response to his insulting remarks. All her strength was behind the hand that seemed to race through the air of its own volition to land a stinging smack upon his cheek. The sound seemed to echo around the room as she stared with terrified fascination at the imprint of her palm growing red against his brown cheek.

She had sufficient time to notice a flicker of fury igniting in his eyes before, with the swiftness of a cobra, he struck, pulling her hard into his arms, tightening his grip around her body until she was so closely locked to him she could not distinguish her own heartbeats from his. His kiss was a lash against her mouth, cutting until her lips felt raw, the acid sting forcing from her a moan of pain. Then roughly he pushed her away, setting her down with a roughness that jarred her spine. She wanted to cry, yet managed to spit across the space dividing them:

'You're a sadistic brute who enjoys inflicting pain!'

He laughed, a hard, dispassionate sound that served to increase her loathing. 'And you, mademoiselle, are a masochist who welcomes punishment as a penance.'

'Welcomes? Never!' she choked. 'My only hope is that in time I may become numb, as a body becomes numb to torture.'

'In which case,' he assured her dryly, 'I shall be left with no option but to double the dose!'

It was a bleak morning with a cold wind blowing from the north-east. Sun blazed out of a sky veiled in dusty mist but gave no warmth as they walked towards the well where the camels were tethered. Dove fussed around the children, trying to ensure that their cloaks were sufficient protection against the cutting wind and eddies of driving sand.

Impatiently, Salim shrugged her away, his excitement intense as he watched men loading a spare camel with packets of dates, dried meat, butter, sugar, tea, salt, coffee and onions. 'Are we having a picnic, Miss Grey?' The words tumbled from lips aquiver with joy.

Relieved that neither child was showing signs of trepidation, she replied absently, 'Yes, dear, we're going on holiday with Monseiur Blais—just a short one,' she added with fingers crossed. Her eyes were upon the vicious-looking animals they were about to mount, huge beasts with spindly legs and upper lips curling into supercilious sneers, exposing formidable yellow teeth.

However, Marc Blais seemed to find them satisfactory. As he finished directing the placement of goatskins full of water, he slapped a camel on its flank and complimented Major Yasin, 'Powerful animals, and in excellent condition! Now, Miss Grey,' Dove quaked when he turned his attention her way, 'if I share my camel with Salim, do you think you can manage to stay on yours with a little help from Bibi?'

When the children fell about laughing her cheeks flamed with anger. Not only the children were amused, the men helping to load the camels were also convulsed by his sarcastic wit. Only Major Yasin, after an initial twitching of the lips, seemed sympathetic.

Dove was glad it was he and not Marc Blais who pulled down the camel's head and showed her how to place a foot upon its neck so that she was lifted up to within easy reach of the saddle. She fought against betraying terrified panic as, perched high in the air on the back of the swaying beast, she forced herself to relinquish her hold on the headrope in order to receive Bibi, who settled with a squeal of delight in front of her.

'Bravo, Miss Grey,' he murmured, eyeing a face tense with alarm. 'Have no fear, camels are notoriously ill-tempered, but this one was singled out especially for you. It is possessed of a comparatively calm temperament and exceptional stamina—which is just as well considering the weight of true British grit it carries upon its back.'

Her answering smile wobbled slightly as the camel moved off in the wake of the other two, one supporting Marc Blais and Salim, the other laden with supplies. They were proceeding at walking pace, yet Dove's heart was in her mouth as she swayed perilously in the saddle, clutching Bibi hard around the waist, convinced that the next roll of the camel would send them plunging from a horrifying height on to a bed of stony sand. But to her relief it did not happen, and as gradually they picked up speed she understood why the camel had been termed 'ship of the desert'. It was a method of travel not unlike that of sailing a small boat in rough seas, plunging and rising, being tossed and battered, experiencing all the vertigo and queasiness that accompanied such an exercise. She was grateful to Marc who, motivated either by thoughtfulness or complete indifference, kept his mount a few paces ahead, looking back only occasionally to check up on their safety. Consequently, by the time he reined in his mount to ride alongside her she had almost mastered the distressing symptoms caused by unfamiliar movement and was even beginning to take an interest in her surroundings.

Gravel steppes had merged into deep sand from which occasional bushes sprouted together with a few dried-up clumps of grass. Gradually dunes began rising up in front of them and as they progressed nearer to the steep mounds of sand Dove began to wonder anxiously about the inevitable ascent. It was as dreadful as she had envisaged. Grimly, she kept tight hold of Bibi when the camel began floundering up a steep incline, pitching them backwards, forwards and sideways in the saddle as it fought its way foot by foot up the hill of shifting sand.

Not unexpectedly, Bibi revelled in the experience, her small body comforted by the feel of an adult arm, her childish mind oblivious to the panic and the dogged determination not to scream that was fighting a losing battle within the girl perched behind. When Marc turned in his saddle to ask with an infuriating lack of concern for her own welfare, 'Is Bibi all right?' she had to call upon incredible reserves of bravery to reply with one brief word:

'Perfectly.'

'Which is more than can be said for yourself, eh?' The aquiline features beneath the roped headdress were alight with mockery. Saving her the effort of a reply, he continued, 'The camels are a trifle lazy through lack of exercise, which gives them reserves on which to draw, but their extra weight is a burden to them in this heavy sand. They will, however, revert to their natural state of fitness in a couple of days.'

'A couple of days ...?' she questioned weakly. 'Is the camp we're heading for *so* far away?'

He laughed. 'It is obvious how little you know of the size of the desert, mademoiselle. In this vast, empty waste a two-day journey would be the equivalent, in your country, of a five-minute stroll.'

His patronising manner goaded her into scoffing, 'You are supposedly a Frenchman, yet you speak as if you consider yourself to be more Arab than the Arabs!'

He looked taken aback, as if he himself had difficulty in remembering his true origin. 'No man can live in the desert and remain unchanged,' he told her with a simplicity she found impressive. 'I have spent more years here than I have spent in France, which probably accounts for the fact that I feel a much stronger affinity with men of the East than I do towards my own countrymen. Imprinted upon my soul is the brand of the nomad. This terrain, cruel though it is, is now my home, I am under its spell, a spell which no other land, and certainly no human being, could displace.'

As she was jogged, saddlesore and weary, farther into the interior, Dove mused upon his words. If his years in the desert outnumbered those he had spent in his homeland he must have been little more than a boy when he enlisted in the Legion. It was hard to imagine the grim, hardbitten man as an impressionable youth, yet the ease with which he had adapted to the Arab way of life seemed to indicate a wildness within that had no place in a civilised land—a wildness tamed only by the maturity that comes with age, and not by the discipline of any human hand. He had come out East in search of excitement and had found immediate affinity with men who were both cruel and courageous, free and unbridled, men with strange beliefs and even stranger customs, men who considered themselves noble and who treated their womenfolk like slaves ...

'I'm hungry!' Salim wailed.

'So am I!' Bibi had been fidgeting for some time; excitement had begun to wane and now that Salim was providing an excuse for a diversion she seized upon it gratefully. 'Can we eat now, Marc, my tummy is rumbling!'

Dove jolted with surprise. The ease with which Bibi had addressed him by name completely discounted her theory that the children held him very much in awe. She expected him to ignore their plea, and was again surprised by his immediate capitulation.

'Very well.' The look he directed towards the children caused Dove a spasm of envy. So he was not so invulnerable to charm as she had thought—albeit the charm of hungry infants!

He chose to camp in a hollow among the dunes where the camels could graze without showing themselves upon the skyline. Salim and Bibi enjoyed themselves enormously collecting wood for the fire over which Marc cooked porridge for them and brewed strong coffee which Dove drank with a grimace, finding it as bitter and unpalatable as the man himself. Nevertheless, she did not complain. Since their escape into the desert she had sensed within him an air of patronage, a conviction that sooner or later she would begin to weaken, which was why she was determined that even if called upon to endure ordeals through fire and water she would not murmur.

She felt his derisive glance upon her face, as, hiding all signs of her distaste, she chewed the stringy meat and soaked up watery gravy with a hunk of dried bread. Then, sensitive to his every change of mood, she looked up and saw him staring with a tense expression towards a mass of low, dense cloud outlined by a rosy tinge as it moved across the sky. Even while she watched the colours darkened to yellow, then red, a huge cloud-mountain within which she could make out great eddies and whirls as it swiftly advanced. The first gusts of wind were tugging at their cloaks when Marc jumped to his feet, snapping the order:

'Quickly, get the children down on the ground with their heads covered. Don't leave them—and make sure they stay put!'

As he raced towards the camels she did as he had ordered and seconds later a curtain of dust and sand swept down upon the hollow, blocking out daylight instantly. In the pitch darkness the children whimpered. With an arm around each, Dove comforted them as they crouched together beneath a blanket, resisting the might of a wind that threatened to tear them apart. Sand forced its way through the blanket, attacking their eyes, mouths and nostrils with stinging force. She felt a weight against her back as the howling, shrieking wind piled sand around them while, in shaken whispers, she urged the children not to feel afraid, assuring them they were in no danger as, somewhere outside in the dark, black void, Monsieur Blais, their protector, was ensuring that no harm would befall them. To her relief, their panic subsided and as she hugged them closer they relaxed against her, utterly convinced, believing her words—*because she believed them herself!*

As suddenly as it had arisen the wind dropped. With great caution they eased their way out of the blanket and discovered a familiar, yet unfamiliar, landscape—towering dunes where before there had been flat ground, filled-in-hollows, rocks that had appeared from out of nowhere scattered across the sand as if thrown by a giant hand. After a couple more silent seconds birds reappeared in the sky and at the sound of an animal cough Dove spun round and saw Marc soothing the frightened camels as he led them forward.

The children, still slightly dazed, were engrossed in the chore of removing as much sand as they could manage from their hair and eyes and paid little attention to Marc as he approached. His face, pitted with sand, showed signs of strain as he dropped the head-ropes and stepped in front of Dove. Sharing such a traumatic experience ought to have forged a common bond, yet she still felt shy of flint-grey eyes that roved her face searching, she had no doubt, for signs of hysteria, and of twisted lips that seemed always to be poised on the edge of a sneer.

But he did not move nor speak. As they stared mutely at one another it was as if two strange spirits met, hesitated, then said hello ...

*Am I in the grip of some strange desert madness?* she wondered, searching frantically for words to bridge the brooding gap.

But it was he who spoke first, two simple words that shocked the breath from her body. 'Good girl!' he said, then strode away.

Dove had received many greater, more fulsome

compliments in the past, but none that conjured within her a swell of awe, humility and pride such as she
experienced at the recognition that for one fleeting,
probably never-to-be-repeated moment she had met
with the approval of one of the tough, legendary
*légion composé d'étrangers!* ...

# CHAPTER NINE

As the day progressed Dove began to feel a grudging admiration for the man whose desert expertise was leading them unerringly towards their destination. Every mile or so he stopped to check their course on a compass, then moved on, always observant, his restless eyes scanning the horizon, noting every movement on a landscape so monotonous she lapsed many times into daydreams.

Once the dust storm had passed the sun had grown hotter. Not unexpectedly, the children became fractious. Dove did her best to occupy their minds by teaching them nursery rhymes and urging them to sing, but they were in no mood to enjoy such a pursuit so, much to her chagrin, Marc took command.

To the untrained eye the desert seems a barren place, but under his tuition both Dove and the children were amazed to discover that the terrain actually teemed with life. Showing a patience she had not guessed at, he lifted Salim and Bibi from their saddles, then crouched with them on the sand, pointing to a mound of loose sand on the desert floor, a crater-like windbreak made by sand grains brought one by one to the surface by a colony of busy ants.

'Down there,' he told them, 'is a bustling underground city full of highways and byways, made by worker ants who collect grains of sand, carry them to the surface and deposit them around the entrance. The worker ants also keep the chambers tidy and wait on the swollen queen whose life supply of eggs is stored in her body. These others that you see scuttling outside the nest are looking for food for the colony. These are very clever ants—in order to make sure they arrive safely home they have a built-in pedometer that registers how far they have travelled and they take their bearings from the position of the sun, just as we do.'

They resumed their journey, and for the following half hour the children were enthralled by this newly-discovered topic of ants, an insect which up until then they had considered to be beneath their notice. Marc Blais answered their rapidly-fired questions with a patience she found astonishing, then when the subject was completely exhausted he somehow managed to discover other items of interest—a female wolf spider picking her way delicately across barren ground, her abdomen covered with several layers of newly-hatched spiderlings; a spiny-tailed lizard whose short, slow-moving legs condemned him to live close to his burrow; a horned viper almost buried in the sand; a fennec, its sensitive ears alert, creeping across the desert in search of food.

They made laborious progress, stopping to examine many different objects, yet Marc seemed to consider that the children's welfare should take precedence over speed. This lack of urgency was explained when, noticing him once more scanning the horizon, she ventured:

'Are you worried that we may be being followed?'

'Initially I was, but not now. The windstorm has

obliterated our tracks so there is no longer any need for haste.'

Hot, thirsty and drooping with weariness, she felt she had been force-marched across the burning sands by the time Marc decided to make camp for the night. He would have continued longer, she suspected, had it not been for the children. But her theory was proved wrong when, as an incentive to flagging spirits, he pointed a finger towards the horizon.

'There is a small oasis ahead, no more than a water-hole, but with a few trees to offer shade.'

Dove could have flung her arms around each of the slender palm trees encircling a pool of green scummy water. The children were exhausted, Salim almost asleep on his feet, yet their energy revived to the extent that they insisted upon helping to erect the two leather tents which had been loaded on to the camel and upon scouting around for twigs and dried camel dung for the fire upon which their supper was to be cooked.

'As a special treat, an award for good behaviour,' Marc offered, 'who would like baked beans for supper —English beans in tomato sauce?'

In response to a chorus of approval, he unpacked from a saddlebag a tin with a label so familiar Dove felt a pang of homesickness that did not ease as she sat around the campfire scooping up beans from a tin plate, rolling them around her tongue, savouring their tasty, well-known flavour.

'We must be the only travellers in this area,' she remarked, scraping the last of the delicious sauce on to her spoon.

He gave a short laugh. 'A stranger to the desert might be forgiven for thinking so, but in fact there are bound to be several camps dotted around. Arabs seldom camp next to a well, they dislike being disturbed by the noise of animals being watered.'

She was glad to turn her attention to Salim, whose head was resting heavily against her knee. The exhausted infant had fallen fast asleep, and Bibi, her small mouth rounded into a yawn, was not very far behind. Quickly sizing up the situation, Marc held up a cautioning hand, warning her to remain still, before lifting the boy into his arms and carrying him inside a tent where a sleeping bag was ready and waiting. Bibi was next; she made no demur as, still completely dressed, she was tucked into her bag which he then zipped up to her chin.

'Goo' night, Miss Grey! Goo' night, Marc ...' she murmured, then joined her brother in soundless sleep.

Feeling awkward, Dove rejoined Marc around the fire. It was still light, but the sun descending swiftly towards the horizon had lost some of its heat; she knew that in less than half an hour they would be enveloped by sudden nightfall. She looked up when she heard a chuckle and surprised a grin which he swiftly erased.

Gravely, he suggested, 'When you wash, I should pay particular attention to your face, which is so streaked you resemble a Red Indian in warpaint!'

Aghast, she swept up her hands to cover her cheeks. What a sight she must look! She had completely forgotten to touch up the dye during the heat of the day, to prevent it from running. How like him not to remind her—to fill his day with amusement at her expense!

Feeling like a clown, she rose to her feet. 'If you provide me with soap and a towel I'll do it now.'

'Over there!' He tossed a nod across his shoulder. 'You'll find everything you need in the saddlebags.'

When he stretched luxuriously and eased long legs into a more comfortable position she stumped furiously away. It was useless to expect gentlemanly gestures from a man who was Arab all through. Still, she wanted no favours, for to be in his debt would be to owe toll to the devil.

Darkness had fallen by the time she had searched out soap and towel, divested herself of the obnoxious Arab garments and sorted through the meagre collection of underwear she had crammed into her pockets before rushing from the palace. She felt a rasp against her skin as she inched her way down to the edge of the pool. During the dust-storm sand had penetrated every item of clothing; she could hardly wait to rid herself of the irritation. Using a bush as cover, she undressed, giving each garment a thorough shaking, shivering as cool air brushed against her warm flesh.

She was kneeling at the side of the pool, soap at the ready, when temptation struck. Why bother to wash piecemeal? Giving herself no time to dwell upon the memory of the thin film of scum covering the pool, she slid into the water and spent a blissful five minutes getting rid of sand and grime.

She felt a new woman, tingling, alert, and incredibly refreshed, when she rejoined Marc, who was sitting brooding morosely over the fire. His eyebrows rose, but he made no comment about damp tendrils of hair clinging to her forehead and grey eyes gleaming with inner satisfaction.

'Er ...' Her glance towards the one empty tent was a giveaway. 'Where am I to sleep?'

With a jerk of his head he indicated the tent. 'In there, of course, where else ...?'

'But where will you sleep?'

'I don't intend to sleep,' he drawled. 'I'll be remaining on guard all during the night.'

'But you can't!' she began an appalled protest. 'After such a tiring day you're bound to be feeling exhausted, and what about tomorrow? If you don't sleep tonight how will you get through another day?'

'Mademoiselle!' he leant forward to chide. 'Don't worry on my account. Over the years I have managed to train half my mind to rest while the other half stays alert. As for having had a tiring day,' he sounded almost amused, 'I was initiated at a very tender age into the rigours of marching thirty miles across the desert in full uniform and with a full pack upon my back. By comparison, today's trip has made as much impact upon me as fleabite would make upon a camel!'

Silently, Dove revised her opinion. He was in no need of sympathy—not with a hide as tough as leather and emotions to match!

'Very well, then I'll get off to bed.' Reluctantly she stood up. Before her dip sleep had been the only thing on her mind, but she now felt so wide awake she knew that if she retired to the tent it would merely be to toss and turn.

'Stay and talk to me for a while, if you wish.'

The invitation was so brusquely given she was tempted to ignore it, but she hesitated and was lost. 'All right.' She resumed her seat, eyeing the dark features made satanic by flickering firelight. 'What shall we talk about?'

'You,' he confounded her. 'First of all, tell me why you were so desperate to acquire a large sum of money.'

Her mouth opened and closed, but she could not manage to speak. She was wishing she had retired to her tent instead of allowing herself to be pinned down by flint-grey eyes that were demanding an answer. 'The ... the money was owing,' she floundered. 'I needed it to repay an outstanding debt.'

'And was the debt paid?'

'Yes, in its entirety. I no longer owe a penny to anyone.'

'Come now!' His laughter had an unpleasant ring. 'What about your debt to me!'

'To *Sheikh Rahma*,' she stressed with dignity, 'whom I shall pay in kind, as was agreed.'

Idly, he leant forward to select a burning twig from the fire. He pressed it against the tip of a cheroot, taking plenty of time as he inhaled, then examined the tip to ensure that it was properly aglow, before tossing the casual bombshell.

'Did you really imagine Rahma would allow himself to be pressured into advancing a large sum of money to a servant?'

Alarm squeezed her throat. 'Are you implying that it was not he who advanced my salary? If he didn't, then who did?' The complacent curl of his lips, the sadistic glint, were all the reply she needed. '*You?*' she questioned, horribly startled. 'But why?'

'For a combination of reasons,' he replied lazily. 'Expediency—because I was in need of a nurse; curiosity—discovering how an innocent such as yourself would fare in the East appealed as intriguing and finally, an urge to satisfy a sudden whim, a masculine vanity, if you like.' He paused, keeping her on tenderhooks while he inhaled smoke from his cheroot, then knocked ash from its tip. 'Many times I have been urged, but not until recently was I tempted,' he continued, smiling as if at a friend, 'to acquire for myself a willing slave.'

A heavy silence fell. As a night bird flew past, screeching in the dark, Dove flinched, reminded of Alya's superstitious fear of such birds whose appearance, she swore, presaged evil.

Through a throat so tight it felt gritted with sand, she forced the shaky question, 'Don't you think the joke you have been enjoying at my expense has gone on long enough?'

His shadow, cast tall by firelight, remained still and menacing. 'I know of no joke. Explain yourself.'

Remembering that from the very beginning he had enjoyed baiting her, had tried in every way he could to scare her into flight, she gulped hard to steady her voice. 'I refer to the feud between Zaid and yourself which was the main reason behind our ridiculous betrothal. Zaid decided he wanted me, therefore you just had to thwart him. It may be that I'm misjudging you, that in spite of your assertion that you are all Arab you still retain sufficient civilised instincts to render you incapable of indifference to the plight of a fellow European being pestered by a man of an alien society. But again, your actions could have been motivated by jealousy, by an urge to discover once and for all whose side Sheikh Rahma would take if a showdown erupted between yourself and his brother. Whatever the reason, it's irrelevant to the fact that a certain aura of intimacy was forced upon us. However, monsieur, you and I are both aware of the truth, which is that for ninety per cent of the time we spend in each other's company you see me as an irritating nuisance, whereas I . . .'

'Don't stop, mademoiselle,' he urged softly. 'Whereas you see me as . . . what?'

'As a taunting devil!' she jerked recklessly. 'A man completely without compassion and with utter disregard for the hurt he inflicts upon others!'

He moved so swiftly and silently it was as if his shadow had been tranposed by witchcraft from his side of the fire to hers. He was so unnervingly close the folds of his cloak brushed against her arms, making her feel enveloped by two huge black wings.

'Wherever is the dove, the hawk will be close behind. Who, I wonder, was misguided enough to bestow the name of the symbol of peace upon an artful little cheat such as yourself?'

She flinched as if struck. The aura he emanated was one of barely controlled savagery, a mood she recognised with quickening heartbeats and a chill of dread. There had been times when he had seemed almost human, but mostly he had been as he was now—as if his inner anger could be appeased only by making her suffer. A moan was strangled in her throat as she guessed at the method he intended to use—kisses that seared her mouth into pulsating life; caresses she loathed but which sent her traitorous senses soaring, his sensuous, magnetic touch which once before had reduced her to a state of helplessness, clinging like a wraith to his rock-hard body.

She stepped backward in a feeble effort to escape and felt a dull ache of misery when his hand closed around her arm.

'Do not desert me, mademoiselle. In the Legion the penalty for desertion is death.'

'I should prefer death,' her voice rose high with hysteria, 'to a life spent in your tormenting company!'

'Death!' He straightened suddenly, the glitter of his eyes showing that for some reason he was incensed. 'What does a simpleton such as yourself know of death that takes men by surprise when vitality is running high?' She stiffened, fearful of an anger unjustly directed against herself, then was able to relax, sensing his thoughts were very far away, when in morose undertone he questioned, 'Why, when no man knows what death is, do we all fear it so?'

Relief washed over her, not so much because of his words but because of the lack of heat with which they had been delivered. For the moment the hawk's talons were sheathed as memory softened his mood from malevolent to mellow. She seized her chance, using the glimpse of unguessed-at humanity as a weapon of defence. As calmly as she was able she resumed her seat within the firelit circle, patting the sand with her palm as an invitation to Marc to join her. To her surprise he accepted the mute invitation, flexing his muscles in the manner of an animal weary of chasing prey before propping himself on one elbow, positioned so that his eyes could read every nervous tremor disturbing her tense features.

'You lost many friends?' she questioned softly, not really caring, simply anxious to encourage a mood which would enable her, if she were lucky, to slip inside the children's tent where she felt sure he would not follow. 'Tell me about them—about the Legion— it might help.' She thought, from his forbidding expression, that her request would be ignored. His eyes were fixed upon the fire, their grey depths reflecting the flames at its heart. She expected words of praise, a soldier's joy in his regiment, so was startled when his voice took on a bitter, cutting edge.

'The Legion has gained renown throughout the world because of a unique speciality—it is expendable. In the beginning, its recruits were drawn from the slums of the world and sometimes from its prisons and they fought, not because they wanted to, but because they knew that if they did not do as they were commanded they would be shot. Today, however, it recruits the cream of the world's manhood, eager youths in search of action and adventure, yet the old ruthess traditions still remain. Legionnaires are sent where no other troops will go, to fight against odds which no other army would be asked to face. And if the losses are horrific there are no angry relatives to question the deaths of men who sever all ties the moment they enlist.'

Suddenly his head jerked upwards and all the heat of the fire blazed from his eyes when he derided, 'I suppose if you thought of the Legion at all it was to im-

agine a desert fort being defended by a handful of
film-star Legionnaires against a horde of Arab cut-
throats? That is a Hollywood myth. Reality is hundreds of miles of forced marches, of menial labour
with pick and shovel while building roads. It is sweat-
ing, cursing, knuckling down to discipline with not the
least reward other than having your throat cut by
some marauding Arab, if you are lucky, and if not,' he
hesitated, the jagged scar outlined white against his
tan, then sprang to his feet, jerking her up beside him.
'If not,' he stared morosely, 'you are left, as I have been,
wondering if there was anything more I could have
done to save the lives of youths who enlisted upon
sudden impulse, perhaps because of some trifling *bêtise*,
*sans doute*—a petticoat, of all things! Killed in their
prime simply because your cheating, faithless sex let
them down!' He shook her hard. '*Mon dieu!* If only
they had thought of the thousands of others who
would have been eager to console them! The Legion
is for men—men who are hunters, with women as their
game.'

Sensing the rage within him, Dove tried to escape,
but left her bid too late. Roughly she was crushed
against a body leathered and lean as a whip, with a tip
of steel to raise weals of pain. At first she struggled,
then ceased to fight when it became apparent she was
only adding spice to the game. He wanted prey with
the courage to resist, a victim that would draw blood
so that he could exercise his superior will, then finally
his mastery. So she willed her flesh to the coldness of
stone, willed her lips to respond with the sting of ice
as his passionately angry mouth devoured hers.

Yet inwardly she was crying for the man whose hatred of women overruled his capacity to love. If such dynamic feeling could be channelled away from hatred and towards love she knew she could find Marc irresistible, for quite unintentionally, he had taught her to distinguish from merely having a body and *being* a body. For years she had existed feeling the hardness of paving stones beneath her feet, the warmth of mittens on her hands, the softness of a cushion beneath her head, but such sensations had been experienced by a body subconsciously numb, deprived of the basic human need of touch—of intimate physical contact. Yet, naïve though she was, she sensed that behind the arousal she was fighting, the havoc created by his uninhibited hands, something important was missing—a bond of attachment, a sense of commitment, the great emotional exultation that comes only with love.

'*Damn you!*' His hoarse whisper penetrated a mist of pain. 'You appeal to all that is worst in me, discover foolishness in a man who prides himself on his wisdom! Stop fighting me, admit to temptation—the fact that our attraction is purely physical need cause you no concern, for it is my experience that a woman can be anything her lover wants her to be.'

Appalled by such cynicism, Dove tore out of his arms, made to feel tramp-cheap by his opinion, not just of herself but of every one of her sex.

'Why did you bring me here?' she sobbed. 'To taunt me, to torture me? I'm sorry about your friends whose deaths lie so heavily upon your conscience, but I am just one woman amongst many, I can't be held responsible for all the faults of Eve!'

Her words had no effect upon the man advancing with vengeance in his heart. She closed her eyes when he reached for her, knowing further protests would be useless, and shuddered her revulsion as his breath fanned warm against her cheek, wishing instead that she was feeling the stare of the basilisk that turned into stone.

In spite of herself, as his hot, demanding lips explored pale, delicate contours an exquisite curve of cheek, downcast lids, the place at the corner of her mouth where lurked the dimple that never appeared for him, a trembling mouth breathing broken protests, she felt resistance crumbling and knew, as passion raced through her body, that here, beneath a desert sky ablaze with thousands of twinkling stars, in this land that secreted the Garden of Eden, the first-known paradise, that could name amongst its brethren Adam, the first man, and Eve, his wife, she was about to be initiated into the art of satisfying a man's violent passions.

Skilfully, as her lips warmed beneath his and her tense body ceased to shrink from his touch, Marc played his advantage to the full, instilling gentleness into his touch, drawing fire from her soul with throatily-whispered lies of love.

She had been transported far beyond the bounds of reason when, through the clear night air, piped a voice, small childish, but insistent enough to penetrate her daze.

'Miss Grey!' Bibi was standing in the doorway of her tent, rubbing her eyes. 'I'm thirsty, please may I have a drink of water?'

# CHAPTER TEN

THE children were awakened soon after dawn by the sound of other children's voices. Dove, who had spent a sleepless night in their company, gave listless permission when they scrambled out of their sleeping bags and begged to be excused so that they might go outside and discover the owners of the unknown voices.

Shrinking from the thought of meeting once more the eyes of the man she had decided, during the long, wakeful night, that she hated more than ever before, she took her time in following the children outside. When reluctantly, drawn by the sound of excited laughter, she edged her way out of the tent it was a relief to discover that there was no sign of the incensed man who last night had whispered furious imprecations under his breath when she had torn out of his arms and fled.

Bibi and Salim were chatting to three other children who had brought a donkey laden with two empty *guerbas* to be filled with water from the pool. The taller of the three, a boy of about ten, carried a stick and was obviously copying his elders as he used it to marshal the donkey nearer the edge of the pool and stood supervising while the two smaller girls filled the goatskins almost to the brim. All three were dressed in loose gowns which were no more than strips of cloth with a hole in the centre through which they put their heads

139

so that the cloth hung down loosely to their feet. Curly black hair, solemn brown eyes and almost identical features identified them as being members of one family—a supposition that was borne out when Bibi introduced them.

'This boy is called Shamir and these are his two sisters, Jazi and Dina. They have walked from their camp which is two miles away to fetch water. Marc has gone to speak to their chief.'

'Good!' Dove had no idea how relieved she sounded. 'Then I'd better see to breakfast. Perhaps,' she glanced towards the three Arab children who were staring wide-eyed, fascinated by the halo of sunshine ringing her bright hair, 'these children would like to join us? I heard you speaking with them in French, Bibi, so as I don't speak the language, perhaps you would like to ask them?'

Nothing loath, Bibi obliged, but her rapidly tendered invitation was met with doubtful stares. A constraint had fallen upon them. Up until her own appearance they had been chatting happily with Salim and Bibi, strangers, yet two of their own kind, but the apparition with milk-white skin and hair the colour of sunshine was alien to them and consequently a little frightening.

Dove put her knowledge of the working of children's minds to good use. Turning her back upon the gaping trio, she set about reviving the embers of the campfire, but in a fumbling, amateurish way she felt sure would appeal to the children's sense of superiority, especially the boy's. After a few moments of watching her bending over lifeless embers, puffing and blowing in an abortive attempt to rekindle a flame, he mumbled a few words to his sisters, then shyly approached, shaking his head to indicate that she was wasting her time.

The two girls, who had scattered to carry out his instructions, returned and laid at his feet the items he had demanded. Suppressing a smile, Dove stepped aside as he laid half a dozen thorn branches end to end and lit the kindling of dried grass he had placed underneath. Immediately, the branches flared and when they had burned a little he coaxed them beneath the cinders, then blew on them until they were glowing red. He then stood up and with a grin conveyed the message that the fire was now ready to be used.

Breakfast time was hilarious. As befitted their station, Bibi and Salim had been taught to use spoons to convey porridge from plate to mouth, but these were quickly abandoned as they tried to compete with the Arab children's dexterity in transporting the porridge in scooped fingers. They were laughing at Shamir's mimicry of Dove's attempt to relight the fire when Marc Blais returned.

Dove's expression froze as he dismounted from his camel and strode towards them. Bibi and Salim ran to greet him, but his response to their chatter was abstracted. She fought back a hot tide of colour when she felt his eyes upon her face, willing her to meet his quizzical, almost worried look which, had she not known better, she might have construed as concern.

'Good morning!' The grave greeting set her nerves quivering. 'How are you feeling?'

'As you might expect me to feel,' she jerked, made to feel awkward and confused by such an uncharacteristic show of interest. 'Only ten times worse!'

He squared his shoulders in the manner of one accepting a burden, then conscious of the children's curiosity he told her:

'These three children belong to a tribe of Bedou who are camped a couple of miles from here. They are the tribe I've been seeking, their loyalty to Rahma is matched only by their eagerness to offer protection to his children. As soon as our gear has been packed we will join them.'

Dove sensed his change of mood as he began packing up the tents; he seemed much more relaxed, and for the first time it struck her how great a strain had been the responsibility of guiding such an important party across terrain where bandits were known to be active and where supporters of Zaid could have been hiding behind any sand dune. Yet he had betrayed none of his worry, had kept them feeling secure and happy, had even joined in their laughter while all the time his keen eyes had been noting the slightest sign of movement, every waving blade of grass, every shifting dune, every camel print in the sand.

Her tone sounded warmer than she had intended when she enquired, 'Is it still necessary for me to retain this disguise?' The look she cast upon her voluminous gown was full of disparagement. Her sweater and slacks —all the clothes she possessed—were rolled up in a saddlebag and, even though their bulk became unbearable in the heat of midday, she felt they were preferable. At least she knew they were *clean*.

Gravely, he considered the question before deciding, 'You can dispense with the dye but, although the Bedou will make allowances for the fact that the children's nanny is English, they will appreciate a show of maidenly modesty. If I were you, I should stick to the gown—a show of boobs and buttocks might be more than they can take.'

Outraged colour flooded her cheeks. In a few succinct words this man could reduce her to shame. The softening she had felt towards him fled. Never again would she be idiot enough to endow him with feelings that were alien to his caustic nature. She wanted to stamp her feet, to scream and yell her resentment of his lack of delicacy, but decided to preserve her dignity by ignoring him completely.

The suspicion, as they jogged the leisurely two miles to the Bedou camp, that he was laughing at her, did not help, but she was able to forget him when before her excited eyes appeared a scattering of leather tents, many tethered camels and goats, and veiled women dressed in simple shifts and shawls going about their chores.

A shout went up from the camp when they were sighted, so that by the time they dismounted the whole of the tribe had gathered to meet them with a tall, imposing chief at its head.

'Greetings, Hamil!'

'And to you, friend Marc!' As they embraced warmly Dove's eyes wandered over the assembled company, fascinated by the shyness with which the women hitched up their veils to hide their faces from the sight of a stranger, and made to feel awkward by men who looked above her head or cast their eyes to the ground rather than stare at her naked face.

When the chief clapped his hands two women

stepped forward to take charge of Bibi and Salim, who were happy to be led away. Dove, although rapidly becoming accustomed to Arab males' refusal to admit a woman's existence except when necessity forced them to, could not help but feel deserted when the tribe, having made its welcome plain, drifted away, leaving her isolated.

It must have been her woebegone expression that caused Marc Blais to smile when, interrupting his conversation with the chief, he introduced her. 'This, Chief Hamil, is Miss Grey. As you no doubt have surmised, she is European—English, in fact.'

The chief acknowledged her presence with a polite bow, then ignored her and addressed his remarks to Marc. Previously, their conversation had been carried on in French, but this time, perhaps as a concession to herself, he continued in English.

'We were informed by a messenger from the palace of Miss Grey's presence and also, friend Marc, of the important part she is to play in your life. As I told you earlier, the Sheikh's messenger warned us to be on the look-out for yourself and the children. The coup has been squashed and in a couple of days, once the stragglers have been routed, it will be safe for you to return.' When Marc nodded as if impatient of hearing what had been said once before, the chief smiled. 'I am aware of what you are thinking, my friend, you are saying to yourself: Hamil is getting old and forgetful, repeating words that have already been said. But there is one part of the Sheikh's message which I omitted to mention and which, I hope, will bring to you and your betrothed great joy.' Dove's spine prickled with a premonition of danger. 'Sheikh Rahma has commanded,' he went on, 'that your wedding is not to be delayed. It is his wish that the ceremony be carried out here in my camp one week from the day of betrothal, as is customary. It shall be my pleasure to ensure that this command is obeyed.'

As the two men, seemingly oblivious to her expression of outrage, strolled away deep in conversation Dove was left alone to control as best she could her impotent rage. Glaring at their retreating backs, she attempted to relieve a mounting tide of fear with the muttered consolation:

'There's no way Marc Blais can force you into marriage; you are a European—he is a European, and as such must conform to the rules of civilised society!' She suppressed a whisper from within reminding her that the arrogant Frenchman was as much a stranger to civilisation as were the men with whom he had chosen to live, and that the rules of desert life had remained unchanged for centuries: women were chattels, slaves to the whims of men. Any protests she might make about a woman's right to choose her own husband would be met with blank, uncomprehending stares.

When a young, heavily veiled woman approached her and shyly beckoned, she followed and was led to a tent, one of two that had been erected near to the largest one of all which, she guessed correctly, belonged to the chief. It was fashioned from goatskins, tanned and dyed with dark red clay, then sewn together and stretched over a square wooden frame made of bars across four upright poles. The edges were pegged down on two sides, but the sides facing away from the sun had been left open. As she drew nearer she noted wind-

shields made of grass matting and decorated with geo-
metric patterns picked out in coloured leather thongs,
wound against the tent pole ready to be unrolled should
the wind decide to blow.

The girl led her inside, pointing so proudly to the
large carpet on the floor that Dove immediately surmised that this must be considered a great luxury.

'Thank you,' she smiled, wondering if the girl understood, and was relieved to hear her reply in hesitant
English.

'At night the ground grows very cold. The carpet will
prevent you from catching a chill.'

In one corner of the tent was a brass tea tray, a
leather box with six tea glasses, and a blue enamel teapot. In the other, a colourful leather bag hung with
strips of matching leather and tassels, enclosed with a
square brass padlock. The girl handed her a large brass
key.

'The bag is for your belongings,' she indicated with a
shy whisper, then twisted round to show Dove how the
end of her shawl, thrown across her shoulder, was
anchored by the weight of a similar key that had been
tied in one corner.

Dove nodded. Obviously she was being told that
there was a need to keep one's belongings locked away,
and as the key was heavy she would have been at a loss
to know how to keep it safe. She could not see the face
behind the protective veil, but the girl's large brown
eyes glowed with kindness. She wore her black hair
parted in the middle and tightly plaited into several
braids that peeped below the fringe of her shawl.
Around her neck was a necklace of coloured beads and

a white pendant made from diamond-shaped stones. Her slim wrists were laden with bracelets patterned with beads, coloured predominantly blue.

'What is your name?' Dove enquired with a smile.

'Naomi.' Her reply was so low it was barely audible. 'I am the youngest of the chief's wives. It is my duty to see to your comfort for as long as you remain with us.'

'That's good of you.' A tremor of fear disturbed Dove's features which the girl's eyes did not miss. 'Though I'm grateful for your hospitality, I'm anxious to return to the palace as soon as possible.'

She did not quite know how to interpret the curious look Naomi cast before quickly looking away. Hurriedly, before Dove had time to question, she asked, 'Shall I make you some tea? You look hot and tired, our climate draws the energy of all who are not used to it.'

Dove certainly did feel tired and surprisingly listless. The children, in their ebullient fashion, had suffered far less than she during the journey, but they had been acclimatised from birth to the heat which she found exhausting, rendering her prone to nausea and throbbing headaches.

'A cup of tea would be lovely,' she gasped her gratitude, dropping down on to one of several large leather cushions while Naomi went to fill the kettle from a goatskin of water that was hanging on a thornbush outside the tent. She tried to relax, feeling a weight of exhaustion pressing upon her lids. The rigours of the journey, combined with lack of sleep the previous night, were catching up on her and it was all she could do to struggle upright when Naomi returned with the blue enamel kettle, steam curling from its spout, to begin in a ritualistic manner to make the tea.

First, she set out the glasses and teapot on the tray, then dumped a measured amount of tea-leaves into the pot, added the boiling water, then set the pot aside to brew. Then she took a conical sugar loaf from a bag, knocked off a piece, and added it to the pot. When it had brewed to her satisfaction she began pouring the tea into two glasses, delicately poising the pot so that the liquid fell a foot or more in a fragrant arc, splashing a head of froth into each glass. She then poured the tea back into the pot, returned the glasses to the tray, then lifted the pot to fill the glasses once again. This ritual was repeated several times before finally she poured a little of the tea into her own glass, sipped, then, satisfied that the tea was sufficiently sugared and aerated, she poured a glass for each of them. Anxiously she waited while Dove tasted, and did not relax until she received a nod of approval of the heavenly brew.

As if concerned about a face pale with sadness, Naomi attempted to cheer up Dove. 'Work on your wedding garment has already begun,' she offered shyly. 'As a headdress, you may wear my cashmere shawl, it is very pretty and almost new—worn only once at my own wedding a few months ago.'

Dove's hand shook as carefully she set down her glass. 'I don't want to marry, Naomi. Please,' her voice held a desperate, ragged edge, 'tell me how I can make contact with my own people. Help me to get away!'

Naomi drew back, rigid with shock. 'I know that your ways are different from ours,' she rebuked primly, 'but even so, I think you should feel more grateful for the honour that is about to be bestowed upon you. Monsieur Blais is a man of great courage, highly respected by the men of my tribe. You do realise,' she peered over her veil, 'that he has no other wives? If he did not think so highly of you he could adopt a custom followed by many of our men whose desire for a woman is keen yet passing, by marrying you for a few nights only, then casting you off when his interest wanes. But this, he has told my husband, he does not want to do. The marriage is to be lasting, binding you together for many years, during which time, I hope and pray, you will be blessed with many sons.' Purposefully, she rose to her feet. 'And now you must rest. My husband, who has the sight of a hawk and the wisdom of a sage, is displeased by your look of fragility. In order that his friend might not be deprived of the pleasure afforded by a healthy and eager bride, he has ordered that for the next few days you are to do nothing but rest, so that when your wedding day arrives you will go to your husband full of freshness and vigour.'

Nothing, at that moment, could have revived Dove's joy of living. Depression and a heavy blanket of weariness were weighing her down. It was as much as she could do to force the whispered question, 'What about the children?'

Naomi was untying the wind shields, filling in the open sides of the tent so that Dove would enjoy the sleep she needed in the privacy of a darkened tent. 'The children will be well taken care of,' she assured Dove. 'Concern yourself only with building up your strength in order that you may delight the eyes and heart of your future husband.'

Dove's lips parted, but her intended argument dissolved into a yawn so prolonged that by the time it had been mastered Naomi had gone. 'Ah, well,' she snuggled down with a resigned sigh, 'there's no doubt about it, I *do* need sleep, for if strength is essential to the art of loving, as Naomi seems to think, then it must be equally essential to the exercising of hatred which, so far as Marc Blais is concerned, is the only emotion I feel!'

She was awakened many hours later by a movement inside the tent. Through heavy, half-closed lids she saw that a brass lamp had been lit and was jerked into full wakefulness when a shadow, cast intimidatingly tall, fell across the cushions where she lay.

'What time is it?' When Marc Blais smiled she felt uncomfortable, guessing that he knew of the furore of emotion she was attempting to hide behind the mundane question.

'It is late,' he told her gravely, totally Arabic in his flowing *burnous*. Dark eyes beneath a chequered headdress swept keenly across Dove's flushed cheeks, sleepy eyes and mouth that looked vulnerable as a child's. Then, seemingly satisfied, he hooked forward a cushion with his foot and sat down facing her. Much to her annoyance she began to tremble. He was so close, too close for her ragged nerves to combat the leap of fear engendered by blatant, rampant masculinity. He wanted her. His eyes were transmitting plainly a desire to own her cool beauty while at the same time managing to retain in their depths a hard core of contempt. He mistrusted her, yet was drawn against his will towards the unwilling girl whom he had likened to a snowdrop blooming in the desert.

His twisted lip curled as he leant forward, betraying in a voice full of soft anger that the frustration of the previous night still lingered. 'I feel like Tantalus, the son of Zeus, condemned to stand up to my chin in water that recedes whenever I stoop to drink.'

Made nervous by a savagery she sensed was too dangerous to flout, she edged away. He was poised on a fine edge of resentment which, if aggravated, might erupt as it had twice before, into a display of sadistic revenge.

However, escape was not allowed. As his hand grasped her chin, turning her face towards him, she glimpsed in his eyes a hint of puzzlement. 'Which is the real you?' he murmured, 'the puritan who shrinks from me, or the seductress whose body melts in my arms whenever we kiss?'

The reminder of a weakness she had been trying hard to forget set a torch to self-disgust which, when she rounded on him, sounded akin to temper. 'Your imagination is matched only by your conceit, monsieur! Why don't you admit that each time you have kissed me it has been against my will *and also against your own*! You seize upon the excuse, "The woman tempted me", simply to justify your own weakness. You hate the idea of being attracted to one of a sex you affect to despise; in common with your Arab friends you have become brainwashed by the doctrine of Adam's fall from innocence, using it as a vindication of the contemptible way in which you treat all women!'

When his eyes narrowed she tensed, expecting him at any moment to spring, to inflict characteristically cruel chastisement, but as the silence lengthened he remained still. When, eventually, he did speak, his words proved that his dislike of her sex was iron bitten deep into his soul.

'Arabs, although they regard Eve as the mother of mankind, still consider her to be the instrument through which sin and corruption entered the world. Women are blamed, and rightly so, for without them there would be none of the lusts with which men have to contend. However, life is a struggle between the spirit and the flesh. A man has needs which, if they cannot be contained, must be satisfied, therefore he marries, for it is better to marry than to burn.'

For a moment the implication of his remarks escaped her, then, as she stared into an implacable face with rock-hard jaw and derisive mouth, realisation dawned.

'You can't mean that you're considering marriage—between *us*?' she gasped, wide-eyed with horror. 'I won't have any part of it!' she stormed. 'I shall absolutely refuse even to attend the ceremony, run away, if I have to, far into the desert, rather than submit to further humiliating ceremonies, meaningless though they are!'

Anger suddenly left him. Showing an infuriating glint of amusement, he assured her, 'The bride plays no part in the actual marriage ceremony. And as for running away,' he grinned, 'such action would be thoroughly approved by the Bedou, for unwittingly you would be carrying out a tradition followed by all Bedou brides who, to prove proper maidenly modesty, run screaming into the desert hotly pursued by the women of the tribe and have to be dragged back by the hair and thrown into the arms of their waiting husbands.'

Dove stared, believing every word. Nothing was impossible in this barbaric country!

'Now that that argument has been settled,' he permitted himself a smile, 'there is just one subject I wish to broach, and that is the very formal manner in which you insist upon addressing me. The mind of the Bedou, like the terrain he inhabits, is free and uncluttered, which makes him a hard man to deceive. You will in future address me as Marc and I shall call you Dove—a ridiculous misnomer, as I have remarked once before.'

For some unknown, nerve-racking reason, this enraged her more than anything else he had said. 'How dare you!' she spat. 'To pass such an opinion implies an intimate knowledge of my character that you neither possess nor deserve. I will tell you, simply to disprove your theory, that my name is made up of the two first letters of my parents' names—Donald and Vera.'

'You have parents?'

She gained a small sense of victory when his eyebrows winged with surprise. 'I have,' she told him bitterly. 'Unlike you, I was not fashioned out of granite and camel hide!'

Ignoring the insult, he stood up, pulling her with him and retaining his hold upon her arm until she was positioned beneath a pool of light cast by the swinging overhead lamp.

*'Eh bien, ma petite,'* he murmured, seemingly quite at ease. 'According to Arab custom it is forbidden for us to see one another during the next three days, but soon the omission you mentioned will be remedied. You will have no cause to complain about our lack of intimacy when next we meet—on our

wedding day. Until then, may *le bon dieu* grant me restraint.' With a suddenness that caught her completely off guard she was jerked into his arms and lips unprepared for his kiss were brushed with the mocking murmur, *'But not just yet ...!'*

# CHAPTER ELEVEN

FOR three days the camp had been alive with the sound of festivity as the men of the tribe indulged in the feasting and revelry from which the women were completely barred. Incarcerated inside her tent, Dove had been forced to rest until she had reached a state bordering on screaming boredom which, on the morning of the fourth day, was relieved only slightly when Naomi entered the tent laden with a confusing array of paraphernalia.

Dove looked up, her grey eyes sparkling indignation.

'Oh, how well you look!' Naomi dropped her bundles and clapped her hands. 'My husband is a very wise man, is he not?'

'I needed a rest,' Dove agreed dryly, 'but I didn't expect to be entombed, or made a prisoner. For heaven's sake, when am I to be allowed to leave this tent? I'm not used to inactivity, it's driving me mad!'

'Today.' Naomi smiled, patting a bundle she had retrieved from the floor. 'In here is your wedding dress. I have come to prepare you for the ceremony.'

Shock stopped Dove from replying. In spite of having lived with the threat of marriage to Marc Blais hanging over her head for the past three days she had never let herself believe that it could really happen. Somehow, something or someone would come to her aid, she had comforted herself, because this was the age of women's liberation, slavery had long since been abolished, any outcome other than freedom was unthinkable!

As, almost reverently, Naomi unfolded from the bundle a gown fashioned out of flimsy white silk, she explained in a high, excited voice, 'Before donning your finery we must wash your feet in a clean vessel and sprinkle the water in the corners of the tent so that a blessing may result from this. We will then brighten your face, adorn your eyes with kohl, and stain your hands and feet with henna. You may have noted,' she chattered on, confusing Dove utterly, 'that nothing you have eaten during the last three days has contained mustard, vinegar, or sour apples.'

It was really too much of an effort to enquire why these items had been banned, so dumbly, storing up her defiance for later, Dove submitted to Naomi's ministrations. But when the girl reached for the henna she rebelled.

'No, thank you, Naomi,' she stepped out of reach, clasping her hands behind her back.

'But you must!' the girl protested. 'Henna is an essential protection against the devil who, if he is allowed, will make husband and wife fight!' Unable to understand the reason behind Dove's hollow laughter, she persisted, 'Please, let me smear just a little on your hands and feet.'

But Dove was adamant. 'No henna,' she insisted, determined to win at least one small battle.

'Then take this.' With a worried frown, Naomi handed over an amulet. 'Slip it beneath the nuptial bed. Inside the tent that has been prepared for yourself and your husband I have left an egg which you must break as soon as you cross the threshold in order to induce fertility, for if you fail to give your husband a son your residence under his roof will be of short duration.'

To calm her, Dove nodded agreement, while privately resolving that at whatever cost the egg must remain intact!

When Naomi slipped the gown over her head Dove was shocked. It was sheer—high-necked, long-sleeved, with a skirt that fell to her ankles—yet was so transparent it revealed every curve of breasts, waist, and thigh. 'I couldn't possibly go outside wearing this!' she gasped. 'How, when you Arabs are so notoriously prudish, can you justify the wearing of such a revealing gown?'

'It is for your husband's eyes alone!' Naomi was scandalised. 'Although the nuptial tent is but a short distance away, you will be heavily veiled and cloaked so that your beauty is concealed from all other eyes but his.' She stepped back, offering Dove a small hand mirror. 'Well, what do you think? Are you not a glowing bride?'

Not even to please Naomi could Dove feign interest in her reflected image. Grey eyes looked alien behind heavy rings of kohl. Stars and crescents fashioned out of wafer-thin gold—good luck charms loaned by the women of the tribe—fringed her forehead and perched incongruously on top of her head was a cardboard crown over which was to be draped her headdress, the fine cashmere shawl Naomi was holding in readiness, draped fondly over her arm.

'You are pleased?' Naomi almost pleaded.

Dove shrugged. 'All this means nothing to me, I'm completely indifferent.'

The girl looked worried, her lips parted as if to speak, but she changed her mind. Then prodded by an urge to help, she blurted, 'I sense that all is not well between yourself and Monsieur Blais—however, desire in the eyes of a bride can be a strong power.'

She had not thought it possible for Dove's face to whiten even more, yet it looked ashen when she murmured, a far from happy bride, 'Perhaps, Naomi, but from the satisfaction of desire can arise despair . . .'

Muffled up to the eyes in a cloak and many scarves, she was later escorted by the women of the tribe to the tent that had been specially erected for the bridal pair. It was similar in size to the one she had left, the floor carpeted as before, but taking pride of place was a sleeping couch draped with blue silken covers embroidered with the lucky bridal omens of stars, crescents and circles denoting everlasting love. In the centre of the tent was a chair—the throne on which the queen was to await her king—but after Naomi had ushered out the giggling women, she dared to confess:

'There is a spyhole in the wall of the tent through which we can watch the festivities. It is not allowed, but some of us disobey the rules now and again, for how,' her slim shoulders lifted in an artless shrug, 'if we are unaware of what pleases our men, are we to know, when our turn comes around, how to give them pleasure?'

Feeling like a trussed and painted doll, and with the same lack of emotion, Dove joined Naomi who was peering out of one of two holes that had conveniently appeared, at just the right height, in the wall of the tent. They looked out on to a man-made arena, a circle of pushing, shoving, gesticulating men whose attentions were pinned upon two animals pacing the perimeter of the circle made by the crowd. The animals were rams with twisted horns and tails hanging heavily with fat, their skins shorn almost to a shave.

'Make way, make way for the lion of the desert!' called out a man in charge of one of the rams. 'Make way, and see how my warrior will devour the miserable goat of my adversary!'

The man in charge of the other ram jeered and shouted back praises of his ram. 'My ram could fight an elephant, if there were any in this barren desert!'

They then released the rams and skipped out of the way as, with fire in their eyes, the rams began butting each other. One ran round the circle and charged at his enemy. Repeatedly, they rose on their hind legs, thudding once, twice, three times before, to Dove's horror, their horns became entwined. Sickened, yet unable to force her eyes away, she watched the two owners separate the rams who, once they were released, ran backward, then hurled themselves against each other with renewed fury. Dove's heart thudded in time with drums beating out an hypnotic rhythm, the sound rising above the noise of men shouting themselves hoarse as they formed into rival camps, urging on the ram of their choice.

Dove's sympathies were with the smaller ram, so she felt heartened when it began beating its larger opponent towards the edge of the circle. Panting and foaming, the larger animal, maddened by the pain of a broken horn, charged like a demon at the little ram which, much to her relief, avoided the thud, gave him a broadside and brought him to his knees. Painfully, he rose, only to receive some more of the same treatment. Defeated, he retreated not just to the edge of the circle but straight through the crowd and into the desert where he could nurse his pain in peace.

When a rich throaty roar erupted from the throats of the men Dove turned aside, aching with pity for both animals, the vanquished and the victorious, angered by the barbaric pageant enacted for the enjoyment of savages, one of whom would shortly make his way into the tent to proclaim himself her husband!

'I must leave you now.' Naomi frowned, worried by the bride's unseemly lack of emotion. 'After the men have finished eating they will accompany the bridegroom three times around the nuptial tent, banging it with canes to expel any evil spirits that might have found entrance within. Only when they are certain it is safe will the bridegroom be allowed inside.'

'Must you go?' Dove pleaded as Naomi made her way towards the exit. 'They'll be eating for hours yet, stay and talk to me, *please*!'

'I cannot!' Naomi wrung her hands, moved almost to tears. 'Tonight my husband has commanded that I wait upon him. I must have time to prepare.'

Feeling mentally and physically frozen, Dove sank into the chair. Night had fallen and the air had grown chilly. She huddled into the cloak, trying to instil warmth into a body unacclimatised to sudden, vicious cold, completely unprotected by the diaphanous gown.

For what seemed hours the men's meal dragged on, yet she could not bring herself to care about the fact that she could no longer move limbs grown stiff with cold, nor even find the energy to move her position on the hard, unyielding chair.

When finally a sound penetrated her frozen stupor, the sound of many footsteps circling the tent, of sticks smacking hard against the leather, she felt too ill to care. Cold had numbed every nerve so that she was incapable of moving so much as an eyelid when the tent curtain parted and her bridegroom stood inside.

'*Mon dieu!*' She wondered if she had dreamt the fierce whisper. 'What have they done to you!'

She cried out in agony when he jerked her to her feet and began forcing her to walk, stopping every now and again to massage her limbs, carrying out the exercise until he was satisfied that blood was once more coursing hot and vital through her veins.

'*Idiote!*' he ground, before scooping her into his arms to deposit her on the couch. He lay down beside her, wrapping her so tightly against him with his heavy cloak she could feel the thud of his heartbeats, the heavenly warmth of him flowing into her body, the strength of arms enfolding her like protective wings.

Compassion gained him victory where force would not. With a sigh of contentment she relaxed against him and slept, unaware that her childish trust had condemned him to endure a night, prolonged as a lifetime, crammed with frustrated doubts.

Her sleep was relaxed yet not undisturbed; many times during the night she stirred, her mind vaguely troubled, only to be comforted with a soothing murmur, a tightening of cradling arms and even once a feather-light kiss upon her eyelids. But when morning came she opened her eyes and found herself alone. She jerked upright, staring dazedly at the wedding gown she still wore, then long and hard at the pillow next to her own bearing an indentation where a dark head had rested.

In that startling second dreams became reality.

She had spent the night in Marc's arms; the warmth, the tenderness, the cosseting she had imagined were part of a beautiful dream had unbelievably occurred! Her cheeks burned as, searching her mind, she re-called pressing close to a rock-hard body in search of warmth, of rubbing her cheek against a chest downed with fine hairs, that had tickled her nose and made her want to sneeze; the drumbeat thudding in her ears had not been an echo retained from the festivities but the beat of his heart, a steady, even throb that had not been allowed to accelerate even though the temptation must have been great!

She was still staring blankly into space when he entered the tent looking well-groomed and freshly shaven. When he saw that she was awake he crossed over to the couch and without speaking sat down on its edge. Slowly, quizzically, he took stock of her anxious face.

'How are you this morning?' he asked gravely. 'Feeling any after-effects?'

'None at all,' she stumbled, mentally adding: *unless you count dismay and burning embarrassment*!

'Good.' His reply was absent. A tide of colour swept into her cheeks. There was something in his look she did not understand, it was as if he were examining thoroughly a face he had never seen before, his interest as intense as his concentration. When she could no longer bear the pulsating silence, she blurted:

'I seem to recall ... I vaguely remember ...'

'Spending the night in the arms of your husband?' he helped out dryly.

'Yes ... No! That's silly,' she stammered, 'because for one thing, I don't consider that you are my husband and for another, we didn't spend the night together—at least ...'

'Not in the sense I had intended.' Once again he deliberately misinterpreted her thoughts.

Confused colour stampeded in her cheeks. 'You're purposely trying to embarrass me,' she told him with an attempted dignity. Suddenly aware of the see-though quality of her gown, she reached for the bed-cover and pulled it up to her chin, directing a glare of indignation his way.

To her dismay he responded by reaching out to tug the blue cover with its spattering of symbolic charms out of her tightly clenched fists. 'How like a woman,' he regarded her coolly, 'to spend hours in a man's arms and then pretend coyness in the light of day. Night madness, daylight sanity, is that it?'

Feeling naked under his clinical eye, she gasped, 'Why must you insist upon implying an intimacy that doesn't exist? All right,' she became reckless, 'I admit that we spent the night together, but as a brother and sister would, as two strangers might if they were forced by circumstances, as we were.'

She had no idea what she had said to light the kindling of flame that flickered dangerously in his eyes as he leant closer, sending her cowering into the cushions.

'As two strangers might! That is exactly it! If I allow you out of here with the bloom of naïveté still upon your cheeks the sharp-eyed Bedouin will not be deceived. Woman of the East are taught guile in their cradles, but you, grey dove, carry an aura of innocence that only a man's passion will erase. I give you a choice —accompany me on the honeymoon Rahma insists we must share, or remain here in the camp where, if I am to retain the respect of my friends, I must parade before them a wife who is seen to be submissive, adoring, and much loved.'

Dove was left in no doubt that he meant every word of the steadily uttered ultimatum. His pride was as fierce as that of any true son of Adam, a pride he would retain at whatever cost to herself. She swallowed to clear her throat of fluttering panic and managed to whisper :

'A honeymoon, you said? But where ... and what about the children?'

'There is an oasis just a day's ride from here where we can stay long enough to satisfy Rahma that the proprieties have been observed. The children are perfectly happy here; a helicopter will be sent to pick them up as soon as their father decides it is safe for them to return to the palace.' He rose to his feet, anticipating her decision. 'I'll leave you to get ready—don't be long, I want to set off before the whole camp is astir.'

She fumbled her way into the loose shift and cloak Marc had left beside the couch, then, winding a long scarf Arab-fashion around her head, she hurried from the tent wishing, as she approached his waiting figure, that she could say goodbye to the children yet reluctant to waken them at such an early hour.

There were very few of the tribe about as they left the camp to cross the lonely desert. It was a grey morning with little wind, the beginning of a day that was to pass almost entirely in silence. For the first few hours Dove hardly noticed, glad of the opportunity to sort out her thoughts, to become accustomed once more to the rolling gait of the camel, and to plan for the future, plans that did not include Marc Blais, the desert, or even the children. She had to return home. She would take the best-paid job she could find, then clear off the debt she owed him in small but regular instalments. She did him the justice of owning that he cared nothing for the money; he had simply wanted a hold over her, an incentive to make her stay. But that was now impossible. Nothing on earth, she decided, could induce her to remain for a day longer than was necessary. *She dared not!* Not when she had committed the ultimate folly of falling in love with a man whom she had been expressly forbidden to love, a desert nomad who valued his freedom above all else, a man, what was more, who could not hide his contempt for every member of her sex.

She had come to terms with the fact that morning, had allowed her honest heart to acknowledge that last night, althoug the happiest she had ever spent, had not been enough. She had wanted more, *much more*! Which was why she had to get away before the taunting devil discovered her secret.

Marc gave no clue to the thoughts that cast a morose

shadow across his features. He spared sufficient attention to help Dove dismount from the camel when they stopped to prepare a meal, enquired once if her head was sufficiently protected from the sun but otherwise, as they travelled weary, hot miles of uninhabited sand, she might, so far as he was concerned, have been invisible.

Just when she was sure she had reached the end of her endurance they came upon a well trodden track. Her spirits lightened but after a while began to droop again as they journeyed further miles without seeing a sign of habitation. Fatigue was an ache throbbing through her body when at last she caught a glimpse of green, then distinguished fields of wheat being watered from trip buckets raised from wells by animals descending ramps.

The oasis extended for about two miles, a settlement consisting of five villages made up of small houses linked by narrow thoroughfares and twisting lanes. Watchers stared curiously as they passed, following with their eyes until they stopped outside the courtyard of the largest house on the outskirts of the village.

In silence, Marc produced a key that unlocked a huge oaken door leading into an open courtyard with, standing in one corner, a well of brackish water, and in the other an old sycamore tree. Curiously, Dove studied the front of the house whose windows were screened by fine lattice work before, giving her no time to linger, he ushered her through the door into a room floored with marble mosaic, holding a cool, tinkling fountain in its centre.

'Wait here,' he instructed. 'This house has been

loaned to us by a friend of Hamil's who is at present spending a few weeks in the desert. A servant has been left in charge, I believe, I'll see if I can rout him out.'

'Why not ring for him?' she suggested.

He almost smiled. 'There is no bell. According to the Prophet, a bell is an instrument of the devil, so angels can never reside in any house where one exists.'

'How ... interesting,' she replied, feeling a sudden shyness at the thought of being alone with him except for one unobtrusive servant.

As his steps receded down the passageway she began to explore. The few rooms were simply furnished, floors spaced with rugs and low divans running along most of the walls, some of which were panelled and some tiled. Ceilings were crossed by massive beams painted dark red. Upstairs, she was surprised to discover, there were no bedrooms—or rather, no rooms furnished as such. Just bare walls and a scattering of rugs.

She started when Marc spoke from across her shoulder. 'The only fittings an Arab asks for the night consist of a mattress and pillow, perhaps a blanket in the winter and a mosquito net in summer, the whole of which is rolled up each morning and deposited in some nearby cupboard.'

Nervously, she twirled to face him. 'Did you find the servant?'

'Yes, he is preparing us a meal. However, anticipating your request for a wash, I have instructed him to heat some water first.'

'Thank you,' she smiled her gratitude. Then on impulse, 'How I wish there were shops—there are so many things I need.'

'There are shops,' he surprised her, 'of a kind. No settlement is complete without its bazaar. After we've eaten I'll take you there.'

'But I have no money!' she protested.

'You have your dowry,' he reminded her coolly. 'It is packed in the saddlebag.'

She flushed. 'Now you're making fun of me. You know as well as I do that the Arab marriage ceremony is invalid, you owe me nothing.'

'I disagree,' he gritted. She quivered, sensing a return of the anger she dreaded. 'Were it not that money is so important to you, you would not be here in the desert with a man you profess to hate, a man who, whether you like it or not, is your husband in the eyes of the people of the land in which you are now living. You will take the money and spend it as you wish. Believe me, it is no gift; I never pay for bread that I don't intend to eat.'

A meal was served to them in a small sitting-room, empty except for a low, brass-topped table and floor cushions on which to squat—an exercise, Dove thought as every now and again she shifted position to ease the onset of cramp, that called for considerable practice. She ate without appetite, toying with the inevitable stewed lamb and vegetables, refusing rice, then being forced at his insistence to accept a slice of watermelon which she had to pretend to enjoy even though tears were squeezing past her eyelids and threatening to mingle with the juice.

She had washed as best she could in water emptied

from a pitcher into a wide-rimmed basin and had come downstairs feeling, if not exactly refreshed, then certainly a little less jaded, a little more prepared to withstand his brooding looks and cutting tongue. But his mood, when she joined him, was as impenetrable as the forts it had been his duty to protect. He had spoken little all day, and his silence continued throughout the meal—a brooding quiet, a simmering of inner anger that made her so nervous she found it almost impossible to force food past the lump in her throat.

'*Diable!*' He startled her by jumping to his feet and venting his frustration upon a cushion which he kicked into a far corner of the room. 'Must you sit there trembling in the manner of a fawn waiting to be sacrificed? Why do you fear me? I am no ogre, no different from any other men you have known!' He swung round, pinning her with a vicious look. 'Or am I being stupidly obtuse? Is it perhaps my scarred face that causes you to drop your eyes and cringe out of my way?'

'Of course not!' she denied indignantly, feeling compassion as a pain. He was an arrogant brute who would not hesitate to take advantage if she were to try to explain that it was her own unruly emotions that caused her most fear. She had no intention of being his bride for a night and then left abandoned to her fate. Yet her heart was too tender to allow her to use his blemished face as an excuse for her timidity. Using asperity as a shield, she asked:

'Why must you always credit women with the worst possible motives? If, in the past, you had been more selective in your choice of companion you might not today have such a poor opinion of my sex!'

She tried not to cower because it angered him so, but it was difficult to suppress a flinch when she looked up and found dark, intimidating features mere inches from her face.

'Are you implying that you embody all the supposed virtues of womanhood?' Her stricken eyes fastened upon the ragged scar that drew his angry mouth into a sneer. 'Do you dare to declare yourself innocent of committing the two most common feminine sins? I challenge you,' he menaced, 'to put your hand on your heart and swear that you have never cheated or lied to me!'

*He knew!* In that moment of clarity it became easy to understand why his contempt of herself had never been far from the surface, why he had found it easy to believe that she had encouraged Zaid's attention, why he had never trusted her word.

'How long have you known?' she whispered.

'So!' He flung away as if barely able to control an impulse to shake her. 'At least you are wise enough to recognise defeat, to admit that the time has come to be honest!'

She stood up, tilting her chin in a brave attempt at dignity. 'It was never my intention to deceive you——'

'*Mon dieu!*' he spat savagely. 'Try to be original, spare me the impassioned clichés, the classical lines of dialogue!'

In spite of his obvious contempt, Dove carried on, determined not to be bludgeoned into silence. 'When you are angry you do not care who knows it—which is how I became an unwilling eavesdropper on your conversation with Mrs Todd. I was in her office that day because I badly needed a job—you were there because you badly needed a nanny. When she refused to help either of us it seemed logical to conclude that we should help each other. But when I came to your hotel I had every intention of being honest; it was you who jumped to the conclusion that I had been sent by Mrs Todd. In your usual arrogant fashion you took charge of the interview, refused to listen when I attempted to explain, so that finally,' she drew a shaky breath, 'I was made so angry by your remarks and by the method of their delivery I decided it was a waste of time trying to reason with your insufferable arrogance. If that's a sin,' she tossed him a cool grey look, 'then you're right, I must plead guilty.'

He was standing half turned towards the window so that the latticed cover cast shadows upon his face, intensifying sombre hollows beneath high cheekbones, adding sardonic depths to eyes totally lacking in repentance.

'One thing I will allow,' he bit coldly, 'your methods were not those of a professional deceiver. Only a novice would be fool enough to believe I would employ you in a position of trust without thoroughly checking your credentials. Mrs Todd, when I approached her, was appalled at the very thought of your being employed by me, though I suspect,' his lips twisted into a wry grimace, 'that she was concerned more on your account than she was on mine. Which left just one other problem to be dealt with—the lengths to which you were prepared to go in order to obtain money betrayed the fact that you were in debt which, in turn, indicated a weakness of character that could be exploited to the full in a land where bribery and corruption are rife. After giving the matter much thought, I reluctantly concluded that the advantages to be gained by employing you miminally outweighed the disadvantages, provided I kept you under close surveillance. A case of, as the Arabs say : trusting in God, yet tying up my camel. My opinion did not alter as my knowledge of you grew.'

'Your *knowledge* of me!' Dove drew herself up to her full, insignificant height. 'You have no knowledge of me, I doubt if you have knowledge of anyone! One learns about people, not with the eyes or the mind, but through the heart. You, monsieur, have no heart!'

His retaliation was swift. In two strides he was beside her, twisting one hand behind her head to grip a bunch of hair in his clenched fist. He tugged, viciously jerking her head so that he could look straight into her terrified eyes. 'Again you lie!' he rasped. 'Without a heart I could not feel, and I do feel—a vital, hungry desire that eats deep into my soul, a craving that cries out to my mind asking why it is not satisfied, a cry that goes unanswered because the essential truth remains hidden from consciousness. If, last night,' he tugged so hard she almost cried out with pain, 'I had ignored my heart and followed my instincts I would not this morning have felt ashamed to meet the eyes of my intuitive friends!'

She closed her eyes to shut out the sight of a face dark with aggression, an aggression born of frustration, terrified to speak lest she should unwittingly press the trigger that would release destruction. He hovered as a hawk over his prey, then, incensed by her silence, he twisted her hair around his fist, forcing a gasped response.

'Beast!' she choked. 'You follow the habits of your primitive friends by behaving like an animal!

'Force is sometimes necessary when hunting prey,' he threatened, bending his head to stamp a branding kiss upon her trembling mouth. 'In herds, as in human society, the female expects the male to fight for her. Losers are spurned because they are incapable of providing the basic necessities for survival—an outlook common to all females, both human and animal. Which is why the human mating game is as fiercely competitive as any observed in the animal kingdom.'

When he released his grasp upon her hair Dove jerked away from a mouth bent on plunder, feeling herself weakening in her struggle to fight a magnetism determined to dominate her will, only to be jerked back again. 'Stop it!' she gasped, pounding her fists against a chest of steel, hating being treated as a *houri-yeh*. She thought of the only other man in her life, her proud, honourable father whose conscience would never have allowed him to act with such lack of chivalry, and the thought of him brought tears to her eyes. They coursed down her cheeks, adding the taste of salt to his kisses.

Marc's dark head lifted. Curiously, he traced a tear along the curve of her cheek, then seemed to gain great satisfaction from annihilating it with his thumb.

'Are these tears an attempt to move me with proof of a tender heart?' he mocked hatefully.

'I wouldn't be so foolish,' she choked. 'Knowing

you as I do, I've no doubt that the sight of tears is gratifying to your savage nature. I'm no longer surprised that you chose to spend the best part of your life in the Legion, sharing the company of men in search of an enemy upon whom to vent their aggression. *Any enemy*,' she stressed recklessly, 'real or imaginary, but preferably female, upon whom they can inflict physical punishment in an attempt to compensate for their inability to love!'

He released her so suddenly she staggered. He had been flicked on the raw! By some blessed stroke of fortune she had managed to find a chink in the armour of hide that served as his skin.

'What do you know of love?' he grated harshly, 'you who worship money as a god!'

'It was love that brought me here,' she told him simply, 'love for my parents who, through no fault of their own, were threatened with eviction from their home. I would have done anything to save them that agony—one year of my life didn't seem too much.'

The utter sincerity with which she spoke, the fact that she was beyond caring whether he believed her or not, was her salvation. He stared, the jagged scar throbbing white against his cheek, then without further words wheeled on his heel and strode out of the room.

# CHAPTER TWELVE

CAREFULLY Dove folded the last of her dresses, laid it on top of a pile already packed, closed her suitcase, and snapped shut the lock. Sadly she gazed around the room, stripped bare of her possessions, which was supposedly to have been her home for a year. Had she been in this land of Adam for only a few weeks? So much had happened that the day of her arrival seemed a lifetime away. Today she was leaving, being flown home in the Sheikh's private plane at her own request and with the full co-operation of Marc Blais.

Her packing finished, she wandered across to the window to take a last look at shaved lawns whose incredible greenness had reminded her of home, at flowers, trees and shrubs, planted and maintained at fabulous cost within the desert's arid heart.

Which was how her own heart felt—arid, lifeless, squeezed dry of emotion at the thought that never again, after the customary final goodbye, would she look upon a proud face made outstanding by a scar, would no longer tilt at an aggravatingly authoritative manner, or have to fight to retain a grip on sanity when being made the recipient of dynamic charm. Often, since their arrival back at the palace, she had wondered at the speed with which he had had them transported from the oasis back to comparative civilisation. The duration of their mock honeymoon had been one night

175

only, a night she had spent curled up in a sleeping bag on the floor of an empty room, left forlorn and in strict isolation.

Marc had been in radio contact with the palace, he had told her the following morning, instructing them to send a helicopter which was to arrive within a few hours. That had been yesterday. She had not set eyes upon him since—when the helicopter was preparing to land—he had broken his silence with the grim question:

'I take it you wish to be allowed to return home?'

He had seemed to flinch from the small, broken reply which was all she had been able to manage. 'Please, if it can be arranged . . .'

It *had* been arranged, so swiftly and with such lack of fuss she had to keep reminding herself that in less than an hour she would be leaving the palace for good.

Alya tapped upon the door and sidled into the room. 'Mistress Mariam wishes to speak to you.' Then timidly, 'She awaits you now.'

'Thank you, Alya, I'll be along in a minute.'

When the maid withdrew Dove took a last glimpse in the mirror before answering the summons she had been expecting. No doubt there would be recriminations, anger, and downright probing from Mariam—the last hurdle but one before her race for freedom could be won. Nevertheless, the eyes she saw reflected in the mirror were full of apprehension. She had chosen to wear a dress of fine cotton, a slender sheath of green crowned by a bright head drooping with weariness on an incredibly slender neck. She jerked upright. In less than an hour she would be gone; the impression she left behind must be one of dignity.

Understandably, Mariam's mood was petulant. 'Sit down, Miss Grey,' she waved an impatient hand towards a stool, 'and explain why you have decided to abandon my children's education.'

Praying for patience, Dove obeyed, knowing the children's education to be Mariam's last consideration, the inconvenience to herself being paramount. 'The children are rather young to suffer from a lack of formal education,' she sought refuge in diplomacy. 'I was instructed to concentrate upon training them to behave politely in the presence of their elders, and in this respect they cannot be faulted. Your own attitude is mainly responsible, of course, for the awe in which the head of a household is held by his wife breeds a fine sense of respect in his children.'

Mariam fell for the discreet flattery. Preening, she murmured, 'God's pleasure is in a father's pleasure, and God's displeasure is a father's displeasure.' Then, suspecting that in some way she might have been sidetracked, her glance sharpened. 'Now, let us get to the bottom of this nonsense about your leaving us. I am amazed at Marc! I just cannot understand why he is allowing you to go.'

'The decision was mine—not his.'

Mariam's eyebrows soared. 'Have you not yet accepted that a husband's word is law?' she scolded. 'He has made no objection, which would seem to indicate some degree of disenchantment, but if he should change his mind and insist upon your behaving like a dutiful wife then you will be forced to remain.'

Dove stood up, clasping her hands behind her back

to conceal their shaking. '*I have no husband*!' she stressed coldly. 'I am not of your race, neither do I follow your faith, therefore both ceremonies were meaningless to me.'

'You lie.' Mariam's soft whisper speared her to the heart. 'I who truly love, and am truly loved in return, cannot be deceived by empty words. Your denials ring hollow, Miss Grey! Be a coward, if you wish, but bear in mind that however many miles you put between yourself and Marc you will never outrun your destiny. You and he are bound by a bond that will not break, a bond which, legal or not, will prevent you from marrying anyone else ever, for if you did you would feel like an adulteress. Other men will serve only to remind you of him—you are his wife, you *belong* to him!'

Angered by the suspicion that she might be right, Dove scoffed, 'You may be satisfied with crumbs, but I could never be! An Arab's most prized possessions are his mare, his sword, and his wife—*in that order!* I refuse to allow a horse to take precedence. Nor will I submit to being regarded as an ornament, a pretty toy to be played with until it is broken and then cast aside. I want a husband who will treat me as an equal,' to her horror her voice began to shake, yet doggedly she persisted, 'a man who will allow me to share his troubles and his hopes, who will let me console him when he is sad and who will consult me if ever he is in need of advice!'

Mariam's face wavered in a blur of tears, but the snap of her fingers was decisive, her contemptuous words rang clear.

'Fool! Why don't you stay? You *know* you are insanely in love with him!'

Mercifully, the children were still in the desert, so at least she was to be spared their tearful goodbyes. Alya had refused to be comforted, only a few moments ago she had run from the room in tears, unable to accept that Dove was actually leaving. Only one goodbye remained to be said. She would have been glad to prove right Mariam's accusation of cowardice by dodging the last heartrending interview, but she knew she had to see Marc Blais just once more, to feast her eyes upon a face she would never be able to forget, hoping his last words would be kind so that in the barren years that lay ahead she might feel some small sense of warmth when she thought of him, have one lovely memory that neither time nor distance could erode.

From outside in the courtyard she heard the revving of an engine—the Land Rover to which her luggage had already been transported was waiting to take her to the airstrip. She suppressed a sob, picked up her handbag, and made her way downstairs to the study.

The door stood slightly ajar, so without bothering to knock she slipped inside, closing it quietly behind her.

Marc's back was turned towards her as, erect and very still, he stood gazing out of a window.

'I've come ...' Her voice was a mere whisper, so she cleared her throat and tried again. 'I've come to say goodbye, and to promise that I will repay the money I owe you in small but regular instalments. It may take some time to clear the debt completely,' she faltered. 'I hope you don't mind?'

Although she could tell by the stiffening of his shoulders that he had heard he did not turn round. The lean frame, toughened by the rigours of military training, remained tense—as rigidly alert as he had been trained to be during dangerous nights in the desert when one missed footfall, one second's lapse of concentration, could have spelled disaster.

Dove found his silence unnerving. Drawing upon her small reserve of courage, she quivered, 'My transport is waiting. Have you nothing to say to me before I go?'

Swiftly he wheeled, as if her words had acted as a bayonet in his back, showing forbidding features and a grim mouth with one corner pulled downward following the line of the jagged, pulsating scar. 'The money is of no consequence,' he dismissed darkly. 'What is important,' he continued in an unemotional tone, 'is the fact that I owe you an apology which you would be quite in order to refuse because I realise now that my behaviour towards you has been unforgivable.' He side-stepped a low brass coffee table to advance towards her, his eyes scanning her stunned face, penetrating, searching . . .

For what? She wished she knew! A soaring of fear sent her backing away from him, fear that his tense nearness might be more than her nerves could cope with. 'I think,' carefully she picked her words, knowing how imperative it was that she should sound composed, 'that neither of us has been faultless. The kindest thing we can say of one another, Marc, is that we were each in our own way . . . prejudiced.'

'Marc?' He seized upon her slip. Leaving a mere foot of space between them, he wondered aloud, 'That is the first time you have called me by name. Why?' he shot with such suddenness that she jerked. 'Is it because only at this hour of departure are you able to feel more kindly towards me?'

'No one could ever feel *kindly* towards you,' she replied a trifle bitterly, distrusting the angle of a hawk-like head, poised as if to swoop.

He relaxed, yet kept her narrowly pinned in his sight. 'Which would seem to imply that I must be an object of either love, hatred, or indifference.' He might have been thinking aloud. 'If you hated me,' he continued slowly, 'you would have left without saying goodbye. I know you are not indifferent,' he paused as if curious about the swift rush of fire to her cheeks, then shocked her with the casually flung question, 'Can there be any connection with love?'

Dove's heart skipped a beat, then raced to make up for lost time. 'Of course not!' Fervently, she hoped that the tremble in her voice would pass for anger. Fingernails cut into her palms as she fought for control, urging herself to remember that at that very moment the Land Rover was being revved up by a driver anticipating her arrival and that with a little extra effort, just a few more seconds of composure, she would be able to walk from his presence without having betrayed her feelings.

The fierce denial seemed to have the required effect. He stepped away, then swung on his heel to resume his position by the window.

'Then this really is goodbye, Dove.'

She turned towards the door, but was rooted to the spot, mesmerised by the sadness of a voice that continued, 'I shall always remember you as I saw you the morning after our wedding—your small breasts, round as pomegranates, veiled in virgin white; creamy, unblemished skin; large, trusting eyes; the slender, curvaceous body I had held tightly in my arms all during a night so prolonged it seemed a miniature eternity. I promised you hell,' he tossed across his shoulder, 'so perhaps it was fitting that that promise should rebound upon my own head.'

A hot blush scorched her from head to toe—heat born of deep humiliation. Through clenched teeth she managed to accuse, 'You're never satisfied unless you're tormenting me!'

He swung to face her, his eyes blazing. 'Torment was a stranger to me until you introduced him—now we are close companions!'

She stared across the width of the room. He sounded as tortured as she felt! Yet she could be wrong—it was not in his nature to suffer, his role was that of the punisher! This could be a last attempt to break down her defences; defeat was unknown to him. He wanted her, but only as another medal to pin upon his chest as proof that once again he had been victorious.

*In no way* was she going to pander to his conceited male arrogance!

She wheeled towards the door. Her hand was actually turning the knob when she heard him call out —not a command, more an utterance of despair. '*Dove, don't go!*' She stiffened, unable to believe she had heard right, then heard a word so alien to his nature its sound ripped from his resentful throat. *'Please!'*

She had no idea who moved first, whether it was he to her or she to him, but only an infinitesimal second passed before she was in his arms sobbing her disbelief of his fiercely whispered words of love.

*'Amour de mon coeur!'* The endearment pierced her state of blissful euphoria. *'Je me consume pour toi!'* A delicious trembling shot through her body when, with a hesitation she found more consoling than words, he impressed upon her upturned mouth the first kiss of tenderness they had ever shared. She revelled in an awkwardness that betrayed him a stranger to feminine appeal; gloried in his uncertainty as he struggled to cope with a situation completely new to him. In the past he had dispensed rough justice to her sex because he had considered women were deserving of nothing better, but now his passion was having to be leashed, his hard body held tightly in check lest the girl in his arms should become frightened, drowned by a damburst of passion.

Her unconditional surrender stretched his control to the limit. Her lips parted beneath his, returning fire with fire, her body sapped the strength from his as she clung to his rock-hard shoulders, utterly dependent upon his mercy, trusting, trembling, eager to fulfil his every need.

Ragged, disjointed words tore from his lips. *'Mon ange! Je t'adore!'* Words she felt were unique because though they might have been whispered by many men to many women she knew she was the first and only one to hear them from him. 'How I love the delicious warmth of you,' he breathed against her ear. 'You are made for love, *mon bijou*. Is it love, this painful, searing flame that burns so ferociously through my body? Cool, adorable flower,' he kissed her throat, her cheeks, her tender brow, turning her bones to water as he pleaded with rough humility, 'Bear with me, sweet Dove. I, who have used passion only to mete out punishment, must be allowed time to learn of compassion. I feel a great, hungry desire, yet I am afraid—afraid of hurting you, of bruising your tender flesh or, worse still, your gentle heart. Bandits, cut-throats, renegades I can cope with, but you, my love, are a quantity so far unknown to me—your very fragility makes me a coward. Take a savage and teach him lessons of tenderness, *mignonne*, I promise to learn quickly.'

She found his humility confusing but extremely touching. Her whole heart went out to the man who seemed so uncertain, *so alone*, when he begged, 'Tell me that you love me, *ma petite* Dove, tell me quickly, *I need you so*!'

'I do love you, my darling,' she quivered beneath the touch of lips questing, feather-light, over her eyelids. 'So much so that something would have died inside of me if you'd let me go.'

'Thank God!' he murmured thickly, burying his face in her golden hair. 'At last you have said the words I thought I was never destined to hear.'

Many kisses later she was lying quietly in his arms, feeling the rise and fall of his chest beneath her head, almost hypnotised by his powerfully beating heart—listening to the slow, steady rhythm that denoted a supremely contented male.

'The driver of the Land Rover will have given me up,' she sighed with beautiful inconsequence.

Marc almost stirred. 'Not so. I told him a long while ago that he would not be needed.' He sensed her sudden stillness.

'I don't understand,' her brow wrinkled. 'How could you possibly have known?'

He tickled beneath her chin with a lazy finger. 'I didn't, I just hoped.' Anticipating her demand for a more satisfactory explanation, he supplied, 'We have Mariam to thank for our happiness, dear heart. I had left her presence only minutes before you came to me to say goodbye. During the short time I spent with her she stated very plainly her opinion of my method of courtship, stormed at me for my stupidity, then described frankly the tactics she considered I ought to adopt to get you into my arms. "Women of the West are very different from those of the East," she scolded me, "they care nothing for riches or for comfort and ask only to be needed. So tell her she is essential to your happiness and she will stay".'

'As I had tried every method I could think of to reach your heart, *mon ange*, with, I might add, conspicuous lack of success, I decided to take Mariam's advice. As no doubt you have noticed,' he teased, 'it worked!'

Dove shot upright, spitting fury. 'Do you dare sit there and admit that you tricked me? That everything you've said during the past hour has been lies?'

He looked suddenly very serious. 'No, I did not lie,' he told her tightly, 'but I would have done if I'd thought it necessary. I would have employed any means to keep you here for, believe me, there was no chance of my ever letting you go!'

She stared into his arrogant face, trying to reconcile his earlier humble pleas with the note of determination in his voice.

Suddenly impatient of the space between them, he pulled her back into his arms. 'Don't let's fight, *chérie*. There will be times, no doubt, when we will, but not just yet!' When she ignored his coaxing he shook her, showing a trace of his usual impatience. 'Very well, I've admitted I acted on Mariam's advice, and why not? Call me deceitful, underhanded—call me what you will —nothing you say can erase the hour we have just spent in each other's arms, nor cancel your admission that you love me! We belong together, *mon coeur*, I will allow nothing to keep us apart!'

His lips stifled any protest she might have made, his kiss demanding, forceful, positive proof that humility was a myth so far as Marc Blais was concerned.

Without resistance, she melted against him. Passion had made her his slave, she had no strength to spare for anger.

He sighed, sensing the battle was won, yet his tone was as commanding as ever when he told her, 'To-morrow we will leave together for England. In my eyes we are already man and wife, but I am conscious that if ever I am to meet your honest look without a feeling of guilt I must stand with you in front of an altar, in the presence of your parents, and repeat vows of devotion that are already engraved upon my heart.' His jaw jutted, the scar a tight line of uncertainty. 'Will you do that, Dove? Will you marry me?'

She leant to press her lips against the scar that was his barometer of pain. 'Yes, my darling,' she soothed, knowing that she was promising herself to a tough, arrogant, impatient Legionnaire. Knowing also that she would not want him any other way!

# Harlequin Presents...

**The beauty of true romance...**

**The excitement of world travel...**

**The splendor of first love...**

# 3 GREAT NOVELS

## Harlequin brings you a book to cherish ...

three stories of
love and romance
by one of your
favorite
Harlequin authors ...

# JOY
# ROMANCE
# LOVE

# Harlequin Omnibus
### THREE love stories in ONE beautiful volume

The joys of being in love...
the wonder of romance...
the happiness that true love brings ...

Do you have a favorite
Harlequin author?
Then here is an
opportunity you must
not miss!